PHYSICAL INSTRUMENTATION
IN
MEDICINE AND BIOLOGY

Physical Instrumentation in Medicine and Biology

BY

D. J. DEWHURST

Reader in Biophysics
University of Melbourne
Australia

PERGAMON PRESS

OXFORD · LONDON · EDINBURGH · NEW YORK

TORONTO · PARIS · FRANKFURT

Pergamon Press Ltd., Headington Hill Hall, Oxford
4 & 5 Fitzroy Square, London W.1

Pergamon Press (Scotland) Ltd., 2 & 3 Teviot Place, Edinburgh 1

Pergamon Press Inc., 44–01 21st Street, Long Island City, New York 11101

Pergamon of Canada, Ltd., 6 Adelaide Street East, Toronto, Ontario

Pergamon Press S.A.R.L., 24 rue des Écoles, Paris 5^e

Pergamon Press GmbH, Kaiserstrasse 75, Frankfurt-am-Main

First Edition 1966

Library of Congress Catalog Card No. 66-14656

Printed in Great Britain by Cheltenham Press Ltd.,
Cheltenham and London

(2367/66)

CONTENTS

CONTENTS

FOREWORD

THIS book provides a course of study and practical assignments covering the basic principles of medical and biological instrumentation, and typical features of its design and construction. It is based on experience extending over several years in conducting such a course in the Department of Physiology of the University of Melbourne, and is aimed primarily at graduates in medicine or the biological sciences who require modern instrumentation in their work. It has also been used successfully as a conversion course for electronics technicians entering the field of medical electronics, and as a course of private study by a number of individuals.

It must be emphasised that the aim of the course is to provide the student with a fund of knowledge sufficient to allow him to use equipment confidently and competently, and to communicate with electronics engineers and technicians. Unless supplemented by a great deal of further training and experience, the course will not convert him into either a technician or an engineer. Suggestions for further reading are provided at the end of each chapter.

The theory and practical work in the order set out form a logical development of the subject; for full understanding it is necessary to complete the practical assignment attached to each chapter before proceeding to a further one. Provided that some assistance is given to students by prefabricating the metalwork of each unit to be assembled, the allocation of an hour to the theoretical material and three hours to the practical work in each chapter has proved satisfactory. Experience has shown that a course of this nature cannot be shortened appreciably without losing contact with the average graduate student, who has little or no background in electronics. None of the commercial "teach-yourself-electronics" kits at present available is at all satisfactory for the purposes of this course. The practice in Melbourne is for students to work in pairs, each member of the course having his or her own multimeter, soldering iron and hand tools.

Throughout the book, transistorised circuits have been stressed, in view of their enormous advantages in terms of reliability, compactness and safety. At present, however, especially where relatively slow signals are concerned, transistors can be used in conjunction with cathode ray tubes only at the expense of considerable complexity and cost. Accordingly, valve circuits have been used in the oscilloscope constructed during this course. Hybrid valve–

transistor circuits have many advantages, but have been avoided for the sake of simplicity in power supply arrangements.

I would like to thank my wife for her assistance in the preparation of this book, including the draughting of all the diagrams; Professor R. D. Wright, head of the Department of Physiology, for his continued help in the establishment of the course; and Mr. W. B. Douglas, for the photographic work. I would like also to acknowledge with gratitude grants from the National Health and Medical Research Council of Australia for the maintenance of research and developmental work in the Biophysics Unit.

CHAPTER 1

CONSTRUCTION PRACTICE

1.1. INSTRUMENT DESIGN

Physical instrumentation is only a means to an end, and should be designed to fulfil its purpose with a minimum of attention by its user. This implies that it is functional, reliable and compact. A functional instrument is one which has a minimum of controls accessible to the operator, and these are clearly labelled, foolproof, easy to operate and logically laid out. A reliable instrument is one which is robust, requires little or no routine maintenance or recalibration, operates when needed with a minimum of delay and gives the required information reproducibly under all conditions of use. A compact instrument is one which does not impede the operator as he carries out his normal duties.

These criteria can be met by instrument designers; they have been met for many years in the field of industrial instrumentation. Electronic instruments in particular have a reputation for fragility and unreliability which is quite unwarranted if they are adequately engineered.

The case of an instrument should be solidly constructed, and finished with a hard smooth surface that does not take finger marks. Adequate provision should be made for cooling, either by convection or forced air as required, without admitting moisture or dust. For operating-theatre use, an additional requirement may be suitability for use in an explosive atmosphere, or clear labelling if this cannot be done. Line voltage connection should be by a three-wire cable, the third lead being earthed to the metal case and at the power outlet.

Two types of internal construction of electronic equipment are in common use. All the components, valves, and so on, may be mounted on a metal chassis, which gives essentially a two-dimensioned structure (as in Fig. 1.1), or they may be mounted in subassemblies on insulating cards, which are then assembled in a three-dimensional array (as in Fig. 1.2). The second type is more suited to transistor assemblies, especially since printed wiring of each subassembly may replace individually installed connections.

In either case the physical arrangement of components should be logical, so that leads carrying signals are as short as possible. A large part of the wiring will consist of small components, such as resistors and condensers, running from one point to another. Where actual leads are used, standard

1

practice is to employ fine-stranded wire (usually five or seven strands of 0·010 in. diameter tinned copper) insulated with coloured plastic. Red is normally reserved for high-voltage circuits and black for earth. Other colours are not standard but it is usual to employ one convention throughout a piece of equipment. Wiring is laid out close to the chassis except in excep-

FIG. 1.1. Chassis construction.

tional circumstances, and both wiring and small components are lined up parallel to the sides of the chassis or card; this improves access to the circuits and gives a general impression of neatness.

In valve circuits, pairs of filament leads should be twisted together to minimise external magnetic and electrostatic fields; it is most convenient

FIG. 1.2. Matrix construction.

to install filament wiring first. Filament circuits must be earthed, but at one point only in each circuit.

Connections between units are made by multi-cored cable, terminated at each end in a suitable plug. For reasons of safety, power *sources* are always supplied from a *female* plug. There is a vast range of types of multi-way plug in common use, most of those designed for radio receivers and amplifiers being far too unreliable for medical use. The type selected should have some type of lock to prevent accidental disconnection, a cable clamp to prevent fracture of the leads at the point of entry to the plug, and robust silver- or gold-plated pins. Suitable types are those made for use in aircraft; although they are expensive, failures are almost eliminated. Standardisation of plugs throughout an institution is highly desirable.

Coaxial cable is used where signals must be conveyed for some distance. Here again a standard type of coaxial connector is of great advantage. Typical connectors are shown in Fig. 1.3.

FIG. 1.3. Multi-way and coaxial connectors.

1.2. INSTRUMENT DESIGN

Commercially made steel or aluminium boxes, chassis and panels are available in a great variety of sizes and shapes, so that in many cases fabrication of sheet metal can be avoided altogether. Larger workshops, however, normally manufacture their own instrument cases as required, and to produce work of reasonable appearance need a metal-cutting guillotine and a sheet-metal folding machine with a divided head (often called a "pan brake"). Pieces of a case or chassis are assembled by spot welding (which needs special equipment to be satisfactory for sheet aluminium), or by bolting or riveting.

Mounting holes are made in the smaller sizes by drilling and cleaning off any resulting rough edges, or in the larger sizes by the use of a range of punches. A hole for which no punch is available can always be produced by cutting a smaller hole to provide entry of a file or saw blade, and then enlarging to size.

The marking of panels for small experimental instruments always presents a problem. Panels can be sent out to be engraved by a commercial firm or

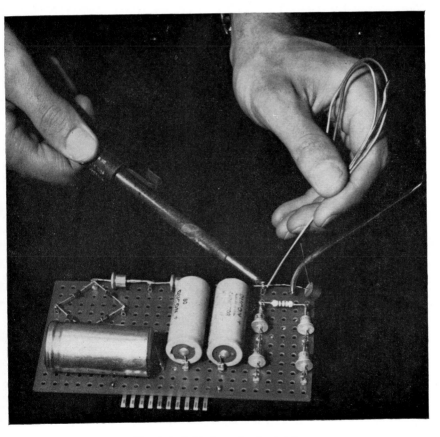

FIG. 1.4. Soldering using heat sink.

can be labelled by use of transfers (such as Decal or Letraset). A very simple approach is to etch an aluminium panel with caustic soda, and then letter the active surface with Indian ink. Immerse the panel in an almost boiling solution (about 2 oz per gallon) for half an hour, wash with clean hot water and a soft cloth *without touching the surface*, and dry with a soft cloth. Then letter it as required, using Indian ink and a letter guide, and coat it with clear acrylic lacquer.

1.3. SOLDERING

Soldered joints form a permanent, reliable electrical and mechanical connection, if they are correctly made. With a little experience an instinct for a defective joint is developed and the practised worker is most unlikely ever to make one. A small electric soldering iron of good but conventional construction is recommended, together with a high-grade resin-cored solder. Flux other than this resin core must never be used, and the solder must always be brought up to the joint, never carried molten on the iron.

Many modern components, particularly semiconductor devices, are readily

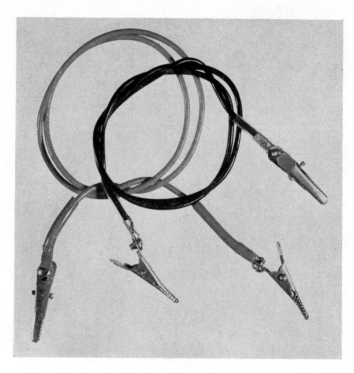

FIG. 1.5. Assembly of flying leads.

damaged by the heat of soldering. It is preferable to avoid soldering closer than a centimetre to the component, and even then a pair of artery forceps should be clipped on to the lead between the component and the point of soldering, to serve as a heat sink. (Fig. 1.4.)

Further Reading

ELMORE and SANDS, *Electronics*, McGraw-Hill, New York, 1949.
ARRL Radio Amateur's Handbook, American Radio Relay League, Concord, 1965.

PRACTICAL

1. Assemble two flying leads 3 ft long, and four flying leads 1 ft 3 in. long, with an alligator clip at each end, as shown in Fig. 1.5.
2. Assemble a coaxial cable 3 ft long with a coaxial connector at either end, as shown in Fig. 1.6.
3. Wire up a nine-pin miniature valve socket and tag strip on a piece of aluminium, using the components shown in Fig. 1.7. This forms a valve amplifier, which will be used subsequently.
4. Wire up the components shown in Fig. 1.8 on a piece of matrix board. This forms a 1 and 10 mV test pulse generator, which will be used subsequently.
5. If access to sheet-metal working equipment can be arranged, the processes involved in fabricating panels and chassis should be observed.

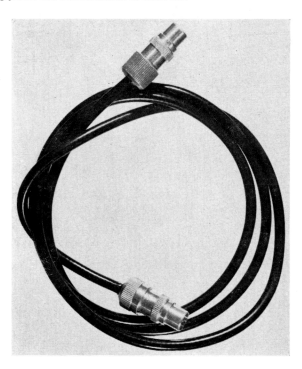

FIG. 1.6. Assembly of coaxial cable.

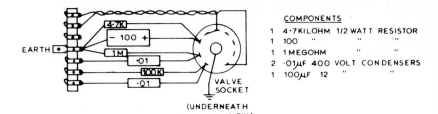

COMPONENTS

1 4·7KILOHM 1/2 WATT RESISTOR
1 100   "   "   · "
1 1MEGOHM   "   "
2 ·01μF 400 VOLT CONDENSERS
1 100μF 12   "   "

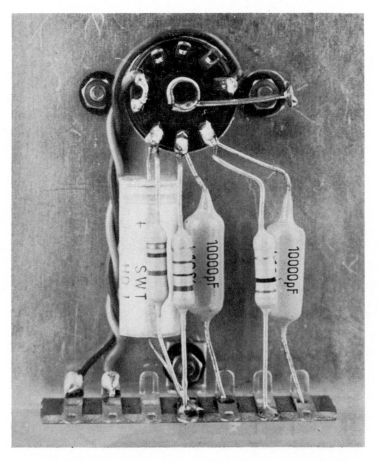

FIG. 1.7. Valve socket and tag strip assembly. (a) Diagram. (b) Completed assembly.

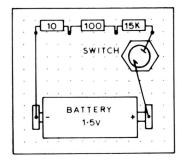

COMPONENTS

1 15 KILOHM 1/2 WATT RESISTOR
1 100 OHM " "
1 10 OHM " "
1 PUSH SWITCH
1 1·5 VOLT MINIATURE TORCH CELL

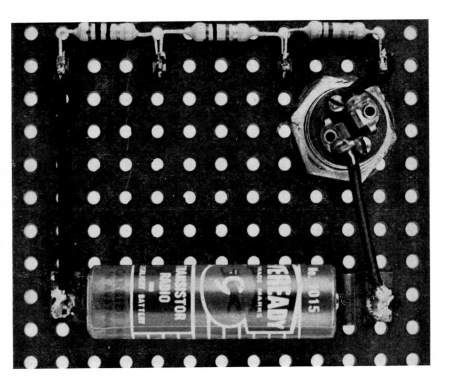

FIG. 1.8. Matrix board assembly. (a) Diagram. (b) Completed assembly.

CHAPTER 2

CURRENT, VOLTAGE, AND RESISTANCE

2.1. DEFINITIONS

Any solid capable of conducting electricity consists of an array of atoms, usually in a crystalline form, whose outer shell electrons are capable of moving from one atom to another. In fact, at ordinary temperatures these electrons are constantly doing this in great quantities but in a random fashion.

If a source of electricity such as a battery or generator is applied to the ends of such a conductor, it is capable of injecting additional electrons into one end, and of absorbing electrons at the same rate from the other. This results in a steady drift of electrons along the conductor, superimposed on the much greater random motion; this drift constitutes an electric current. The unit of quantity, or *charge*, of electricity is the *coulomb*, representing approximately $6\cdot4 \times 10^{18}$ electrons. A current of one coulomb per second past a given point is defined as a current of one *ampere*. If q is the charge in coulombs, and i the current in amperes, at a given point, then at any instant

$$i = \dot{q}, \qquad (2.1)$$

where $\dot{q}$ is the rate of passage of q past the given point, in coulombs per second. For a steady rate of passage

$$i = \frac{q}{t}. \qquad (2.2)$$

When a source of electricity moves electrons through a conductor, the movement takes place effectively against internal friction; work is done in the conductor and heat is produced. If the source of electricity supplies electrons at a pressure such that for every coulomb that passes through the conductor, work of one joule is done, and the equivalent amount of heat produced (approximately $0\cdot24$ cal), then the source is said to have an *electromotive force* of one *volt*. (Electromotive force, usually abbreviated to EMF, is the term used to express electrical pressure; frequently the word "voltage" is used as a substitute.) If now the conductor is such that one coulomb per second, or one ampere, flows when an EMF of one volt is applied, work is done at a rate of one joule per second, which corresponds to a *power* of one *watt*. If W is the power in watts, and e the voltage,

$$W = ei. \qquad (2.3)$$

The power is also a measure of the rate of heat production in the conductor, and consequently a measure of the rate at which it must *dissipate* heat if its temperature is to remain steady.

Finally, if, as in the last example, the conductor is such that one ampere flows when an EMF of one volt is applied, the conductor is said to have a *resistance* of one *ohm*. If R is the resistance in ohms,

$$R = \frac{e}{i}. \tag{2.4}$$

This last statement is known as Ohm's law.

In routine electronic work, charge is very seldom used, but eqns. (2.3) and (2.4) are the very basis of all design and all testing of equipment. If two practical points are noted, practically all calculations with eqns. (2.3) and (2.4) can be done mentally with adequate accuracy. First, it is quicker to work in terms of volts, *milliamperes*, *milliwatts* and *kilohms*, which form a consistent set of derived units, than in volts, amperes, watts and ohms. Secondly, the best way to remember Ohm's law is by the rule "If volts are known, divide into them by the other given quantity to obtain the third; if volts are not given, multiply the given quantities to obtain them". Thus 20 V applied to 5 K (as kilohms are often written) gives 4 mA.

Equations (2.3) and (2.4) are frequently used in combination, to give

$$W = i^2 R. \tag{2.5}$$

2.2 RESISTORS

In practical electronic circuits it is frequently required to produce a known current from a given voltage, or vice versa, and circuit elements consisting of conductors made to have a known amount of resistance are very common; these are known as *resistors*. Resistors are specified in terms of (a) their nominal resistance, and the percentage variation in it allowed by the manufacturer (the *tolerance*), and (b) the maximum power they can dissipate without an excessive temperature rise. Thus a typical specification might be "100 K $\pm$ 5% 1 W". For dissipations up to 2 W (few circuit requirements exceed this) resistors are made of a carbon composition, in sizes of about 0·1, 0·5, 1 and 2 W. Above this, they are made either of a metal oxide or of a spiral of high-resistance alloy wire.

Resistors available commercially appear at first sight to have rather odd values of resistance; in fact they are arranged in a logarithmic series of *preferred values*, with their tolerances overlapping slightly. Thus in the decade from 10 to 100 ohm for 10% tolerance resistors, the values found are 10, 12, 15, 18, 22, 27, 33, 39, 47, 56, 68, 82, 100 ohm, and this series is repeated in each decade.

Resistors are colour coded, as shown in Fig. 2.1, using four bands of colour starting from one end.

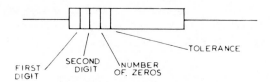

FIG. 2.1. Colour coding of resistors.

The colours used are shown in Table 2.1.

TABLE 2.1
COLOUR CODING OF RESISTORS

Digit	Colour	Percentage tolerance	Colour
0	black	± 20	none
1	brown	± 10	silver
2	red	± 5	gold
3	orange	± 1	brown
4	yellow		
5	green		
6	blue		
7	violet		
8	grey		
9	white		

Modern first grade resistors should be used throughout any electronic equipment; a small economy here will almost inevitably lead to trouble.

2.3 NOISE IN RESISTORS

In a highly sensitive amplifier, such as is frequently used to record the very small voltages occurring in living tissues, the factor which determines the smallest signals which can be detected is the random movement of electrons in the equipment itself. This is known in general terms as noise. Although valves or transistors make their own contribution to this noise, every resistor also contributes, in two ways. The first of these is due to the random motion of its outer shell electrons, as discussed in §2.1. This is thermal agitation noise, which can be reduced only by reducing the value of the resistance. The second is due to imperfections in the structure of the resistor. Carbon resistors are inherently somewhat more noisy than wire-wound ones, but modern high-grade carbon resistors are suitable for most purposes. Usually amplified noise from the resistors near the input of a biological amplifier swamps that due to any other source.

2.4. COMBINATIONS OF RESISTORS

Resistors may be connected in *series*, as shown in Fig. 2.2(a), or in *parallel*, as in Fig. 2.2(b). In the first case the resistances are added:

$$R_{\text{total}} = R_1 + R_2. \tag{2.6}$$

In the second case, the *conductances* are added. If G is the conductance of a resistance R,

$$G = \frac{1}{R} \tag{2.7}$$

and

$$G_{\text{total}} = G_1 + G_2. \tag{2.8}$$

Since it is more usual to work in terms of resistance,

$$\frac{1}{R_{\text{total}}} = \frac{1}{R_1} + \frac{1}{R_2}. \tag{2.9}$$

Equation (2.9) is most conveniently rearranged in the form of "product over sum":

$$R_{\text{total}} = \frac{R_1 R_2}{R_1 + R_2}. \tag{2.9a}$$

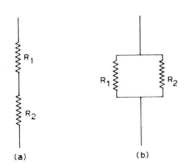

FIG. 2.2. Resistors. (a) In series. (b) In parallel.

In either the series or the parallel combination, the total power dissipation is the sum of the dissipations of the individual resistors. This fact is often used to replace one resistor of large dissipation by two smaller ones; these may each have twice the desired resistance and be placed in parallel, or each have half the desired resistance and be placed in series.

A simple circuit configuration often found is the *voltage divider*, as shown in Fig. 2.3; if two resistors in series are placed across a source of EMF, a fraction of the source voltage will be obtained from the junction. This fraction is directly proportional to the fraction of the total resistance at which the junction occurs.

$$e_{\text{out}} = \frac{R_2}{R_1 + R_2} \cdot e_{\text{in}}.$$ (2.10)

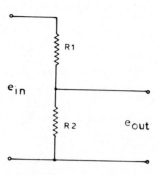

FIG. 2.3. The voltage divider.

This relationship only holds provided that no *current* is taken from the terminals marked e_{out}.

A variable voltage divider, universally (and wrongly!) called a *potentiometer*, is often encountered. These may have a carbon or a wire-wound track, over which a wiper is moved by a control shaft. Wire-wound potentiometers are not usually available above a resistance of 50 K, and carbon potentiometers are used for larger values. Wire-wound potentiometers almost always have a linear relation between angle of rotation and output voltage, but carbon potentiometers, unless a linear relation is specifically ordered, are made to be approximately logarithmic.

2.5. BATTERIES

After almost passing out of use in electronic engineering, batteries have assumed a new importance with the introduction of transistor circuits. The commonest element is still the dry Leclanché cell. This is found in cylindrical form (in which case it may or may not be hermetically sealed to avoid leakage and subsequent damage to electronic equipment), or as a wafer. Either form may be attached in series with others to form a battery of higher voltage. Leclanché cells have the serious disadvantage that their voltage falls progressively during life; they are steadily being superseded by the alkaline manganese–zinc cell, and also by the mercury cell, which first found employment in hearing aids. Both of these are much more expensive than the Leclanché cell, but nevertheless are recommended for use in all battery-powered transistor circuits where calibration is important. The disposal of used mercury cells requires care, since they are sealed, and explode violently if thrown into a fire.

Lead–acid accumulators may be regarded as obsolete in electronic engineering applications, except perhaps as a major source of power in field work. As will be discussed in Chapters 10 and 11, they have been completely superseded for other purposes by electronically regulated units operated from the AC line voltage. Small rechargeable cells, such as the nickel–cadmium or the silver–zinc, are sometimes used to replace Leclanché or mercury cells in transistorised equipment.

Further Reading

TERMAN and PETTIT, *Electronic Measurements*, McGraw-Hill, New York, 1952.
ARRL Radio Amateur's Handbook, American Radio Relay League, Concord, 1965.
SCROGGIE, *Radio and Electronic Laboratory Handbook* (7th ed.) Iliffe, London, 1961.
Manufacturers' literature on resistors and batteries.

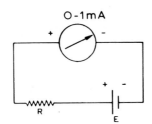

FIG. 2.4. Applications of Ohm's Law.

PRACTICAL

1. Connect up the circuit shown in Fig. 2.4, using four 1·5 K resistors in series for R. Measure and tabulate the current for E = 0 V, 1·5 V, 3 V, 4·5 V, 6 V. Plot a graph showing current as a function of voltage, and draw the straight line of best fit. How much do individual points depart from this line, and why? Using Ohm's law, deduce the value of R from this line.

2. From the results obtained above, tabulate the power dissipation in R as a function of the current flowing, using eqn. (2.5), and plot a graph to show it. Calculate the maximum current R could carry without exceeding the rated maximum dissipation of the resistors.

3. Using E = 1·5 V, measure and tabulate the current for R = 6 K, 4·5 K, 3 K and 1·5 K (but *not* zero!). Plot a graph showing the current as a function of the resistance. Replot the current as a function of 1/R. Why should this give a straight line? Using Ohm's law, deduce the value of E from this line.

4. Examine as wide a variety as possible of resistors and potentiometers, and familiarise yourself with typical construction features and markings.

CHAPTER 3

METERS

3.1. BASIC MOVING-COIL METER

The only type of meter used in modern electronic instruments is the moving coil or d'Arsonval; a description of its principle and construction will be found in any standard textbook on electricity and magnetism. These meters are accurate and robust, and may be obtained with extremely sensitive movements, down to 10 μA full-scale deflection. Final calibration may be affected to some extent if the meter is mounted in a steel panel; calibration for this purpose should be specified if required.

Although this type of meter is essentially a milliammeter, it may be used for many purposes by the addition of suitable circuitry. The basic current range may be extended by the use of *shunts* connected in parallel with the meter, so that only a small fixed fraction of the total current passes through the meter. The required value may be calculated from the relation

$$R_s = \frac{R_m}{M-1},\tag{3.1}$$

where R_s is the shunt resistance, R_m the meter resistance and M the number of times the basic meter range is to be multiplied. In practice, shunts are always adjusted finally by the use of a known current. For use as a volt-meter, large *series resistors* are used, and Ohm's law is invoked to calibrate the meter in terms of voltage. To measure resistance a *known EMF* is applied in series with the meter and the resistor, and Ohm's law again used to perform the calibration. A protective resistor is placed in series with the meter, so that if the unknown resistance should in fact be zero, the meter will read only full scale, instead of passing a destructively large current. The value of the protective resistor is subtracted in each case from the total calculated resistance to obtain the unknown resistance.

3.2. MULTIMETER

For practical use in electrical and electronic testing, a single basic meter is normally converted into a *multimeter* by the addition of a wide variety of shunts, series resistances and sources of EMF; these can be selected at will by a rotary switch. When purchasing a commercial instrument it is the calibration rather than the assembly of components which is being acquired, and a good multimeter is basic in all servicing and design work. It is customary to specify multimeters in terms of the number of ohms required in the circuit to give a basic voltmeter with a range of 0–1 V; the number of ohms required for any other voltage range can then be obtained by proportion. This method, although convenient, is, in fact, merely specifying the sensitivity of the basic meter; thus a 20,000 ohm/V multimeter will contain a 0–50 μA meter, and so on. In modern practice an instrument with a sensitivity of at least 20,000 ohm/V is essential for routine use. The instrument which is to be constructed in the practical session has only a limited number of ranges, and a sensitivity of only 1000 ohm/V; it does, however, clearly show the principles of multimeter construction, and has a wide variety of uses.

(a)

Further Reading

TERMAN and PETTIT, *Electronic Measurements*, McGraw-Hill, New York, 1952.
ARRL Radio Amateur's Handbook, American Radio Relay League, Concord, 1965.
SCROGGIE, *Radio and Electronic Laboratory Handbook* (7th ed.) Iliffe, London, 1961.
DONALDSON, *Electronic Apparatus for Biological Research*, Butterworth, London, 1958.

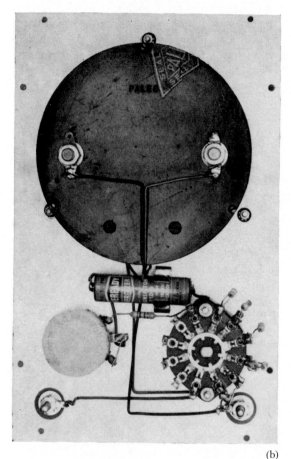

(b)

FIG. 3.1. Simple multimeter. (a) Front. (b) Rear.

PRACTICAL

A simple multimeter as shown in Fig. 3.1 will be constructed in stages.

1. Basic 0–1 milliampere range. Connect up the wiring as shown in Fig. 3.2, in which the two wafers of the selector switch are shown as though they were side by side instead of one above the other (compare with Fig. 3.1).

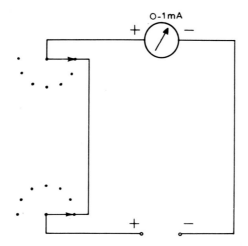

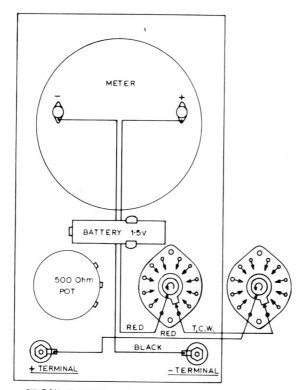

SWITCH IS SHOWN IN 1mA POSITION

FIG. 3.2. Multimeter stage 1. (a) Circuit. (b) Wiring diagram.

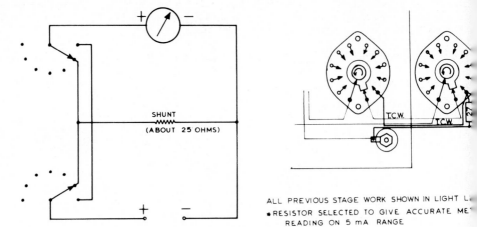

FIG. 3.3. Multimeter stage 2. (a) Circuit. (b) Wiring diagram.

2. Connect up the shunt as shown in Fig. 3.3 to produce an additional current range of 0–5 mA.

Test by use of a 6 V battery and 1·5 K resistor. Does the meter give the exact reading you anticipate? If not, why not?

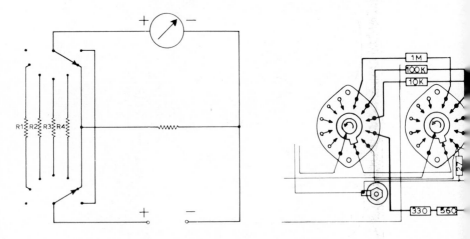

FIG. 3.4. Multimeter stage 3. (a) Circuit. (b) Wiring diagram.

3. Connect up the series resistors as shown in Fig. 3.4, to produce a number of voltage ranges in addition to the two current ranges already in use.

Why is R_4 not 1 K?

Test these ranges by use of suitable batteries, singly and in series.

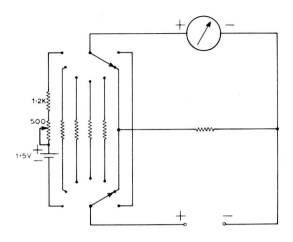

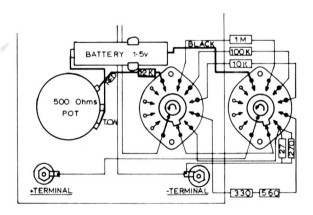

Fig. 3.5. Multimeter stage 4. (a) Circuit. (b) Wiring diagram.

4. Connect up the remaining position of the rotary switch as shown in Fig. 3.5, to form an ohmmeter.

Using Ohm's law, draw a calibration graph for this instrument as an ohmmeter. Use this calibration to measure and label your 1·5 K resistors from the experiments in Chapter 2. Does the result help in answering the questions in that practical session?

5. Produce several series, parallel and series–parallel combinations of your 1·5 K resistors. Using the actual measured value of each resistor obtained in experiment 4, compare the measured and calculated values of the combinations.

6. Examine as wide a variety of multimeters as possible, observing the ranges available on each.

CHAPTER 4

THE POTENTIOMETER AND WHEATSTONE BRIDGE

4.1. THE POTENTIOMETER

This instrument is used basically for the comparison of an unknown voltage with a known standard voltage, and in the form found in laboratories for precision measurement is capable of extremely high accuracy. It may also be adapted for measurement of current or resistance. Many practical versions of the circuit are employed in the fields of industrial and medical electronics.

The principle is shown in Fig. 4.1, and it will be seen that it is essentially a calibrated voltage divider. A long uniform wire is set up beside a scale calibrated in volts, in this case from 0 to 1·5, and its ends are connected to a 2 V battery A in series with a calibrating variable resistor R. Any voltage E from 0 to 1·5 can be picked off the slide wire between the origin and the moving

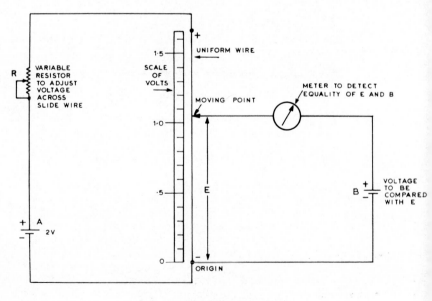

FIG. 4.1. Potentiometer circuit.

point, and this voltage is connected in series with a sensitive meter and a source of voltage B which is to be measured. Since B is connected in the reverse direction to E, the meter will read zero when they are exactly equal.

The potentiometer is first calibrated by putting an accurately known standard source of voltage at B (suitable *standard cells* are available for this purpose), setting the moving point to the correct voltage on the scale and adjusting R until the meter reads zero. The scale is now reading correctly for its whole length; an unknown source of voltage may be substituted at B, the moving point adjusted until the meter again reads zero, and the unknown voltage read off the scale. It should be noticed that when the reading is taken no current is being drawn from the slide wire, and it functions as a true voltage divider (§2.4).

One of the most useful forms of this instrument is the self-balancing potentiometer. In this device the meter is replaced by a very sensitive amplifier, whose output voltage drives a small electric motor, and this slides the moving point along the wire. In this way, if the potential E and the potential of B are not equal, the motor will run until they become so, and this is the desired condition of balance. The moving point also carries a pen, which moves across a chart, which is driven forward by a clock movement. Thus a continuous accurate record of the potential at B is kept. Such instruments are widely used in research and industry; they are discussed further in §27.3(a).

The potentiometer is widely used for *thermocouple thermometry*. If two dissimilar metals are connected in the circuit shown in Fig. 4.2, and the junctions 1 and 2 are at different temperatures, a small EMF will be generated, which will be proportional to the temperature difference, and of a magnitude depending on the two metals. For temperature differences of several hundred degrees Centigrade, the EMF is typically a few millivolts.

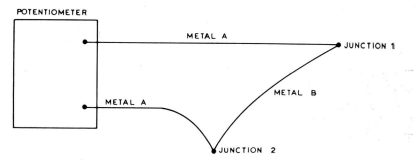

FIG. 4.2. Thermocouple thermometer.

For temperatures up to about 500°C, metal A may be copper, and metal B the alloy *constantan*, which is frequently used in the manufacture of wire-wound resistors. For higher temperatures A may be platinum, and B a platinum–iridium alloy. One junction (the *cold* junction) is normally held at a constant temperature, and the other (the *hot* junction) used as the measuring element. The potentiometer may then be calibrated directly in degrees Centigrade. By the use of an ingenious compensating circuit in many commercial instruments, the effect of room temperature changes on the cold junction is corrected.

4.2. THE WHEATSTONE BRIDGE

This instrument is used for the measurement of unknown resistances by comparison with a standard resistance. The basic circuit is shown in Fig. 4.3.

Omitting the meter G for the moment, this circuit may be regarded as two voltage dividers, ABD and ACD, connected in parallel across the source of voltage E.

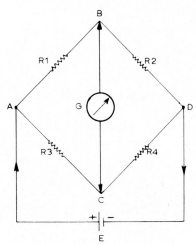

FIG. 4.3. Wheatstone bridge.

The potential at B will then be $R_2/(R_1 + R_2)$ of E, and the potential at C will be $R_4/(R_3 + R_4)$ of E.

Let us find the condition for these two potentials to be equal, so that inserting the meter G between B and C will produce no current from B to C. This will occur when

$$\frac{R_2}{R_1 + R_2} \cdot E = \frac{R_4}{R_3 + R_4} \cdot E, \tag{4.1}$$

or when

$$\frac{R_2}{R_1 + R_2} = \frac{R_4}{R_3 + R_4}, \tag{4.2}$$

irrespective of the voltage E. Equation (4.2) simplifies to

$$\frac{R_1}{R_2} = \frac{R_3}{R_4}. \qquad (4.3)$$

In this condition, the meter reads zero and the bridge is said to be *balanced*.

If $R_3 = R_4$, then balance occurs when $R_1 = R_2$, and if R1 is an unknown resistor and R2 is an accurately calibrated variable resistor, R_1 may be measured by setting R_2 for balance.

Whatever the ratio of R_3 to R_4, the same ratio of R_1 to R_2 will give balance; thus resistors very much larger or smaller than the standard R2 can be measured.

Although the condition of balance is independent of E, the sensitivity of the bridge to a small unbalance is directly proportional to E; further, the greatest sensitivity is obtained when the four arms are equal.

Apart from its use in resistance measurement, the Wheatstone bridge is widely used for *resistance thermometry*. All metals have the property of increasing their resistance with temperature, and the two most suitable for resistance thermometry are nickel and platinum. Both of these increase their resistance by about 0·4% per degree Centigrade. In addition to metals, a large range of semi-conductor materials show considerable resistance variations with temperature, usually giving a fall in resistance with rising temperature. This property is used in the construction of *thermistors*, which are made in a variety of physical shapes, some extremely small, and in a variety of resistances at any given temperature. Their resistance change is not linear with temperature, but exponential.

The Wheatstone bridge circuit is sometimes used as a *pseudo-bridge*, by having three arms fixed and the fourth variable, and reading the meter current as a measure of changes in the fourth arm. Although the meter current is not directly proportional to the resistance of the fourth arm, it is a reasonably good approximation to it over a small range near balance. This is the condition obtaining for many applications in resistance thermometry. In the case of thermistor thermometry, the pseudo-bridge is particularly convenient, since the curvature of the thermistor characteristic compensates the curvature of the bridge characteristic over quite a wide range of resistance variation. For further details, reference should be made to the paper by Cole listed at the end of the chapter.

Further Reading

TERMAN and PETTIT, *Electronic Measurements*, McGraw-Hill, New York, 1952.

COLE, A thermistor thermometer bridge, *Rev. Sci. Instr.* **28**, 326 (1957).

Manufacturers' data sheets on thermistors.

Any standard textbook on electricity and magnetism.

PRACTICAL

1. Set up a copper–constantan or copper–nichrome thermocouple, using a 0–1 milliammeter as a millivoltmeter to detect the EMF produced. (If the meter has an internal resistance of 100 ohm, what is its range as a millivoltmeter?) Observe the deflection produced by immersing the hot junction directly in molten solder (about 300°C). Now use it to estimate the temperature produced at distances of 5 cm, 2 cm, 1 cm, 0·5 cm along a copper wire from a normal soldering operation. Next, try your long-nosed pliers or a pair of artery forceps as a thermal shunt between the hot junction and the soldered joint. Is this worthwhile to protect delicate components during soldering? What is a satisfactory length of pigtail to leave on a delicate component when soldering it into a circuit?

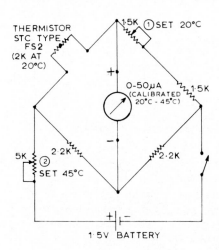

Fig. 4.4. Thermistor thermometer.

2. Construct a simple thermistor thermometer according to the circuit of Fig. 4.4.

Calibrate the thermometer, first at 20°C exactly to give zero reading, then at 40–45°C to give correct reading. (Use at least a litre of water, and stir well.) Test at an intermediate temperature, and by taking body temperature.

(Note that a practical circuit for routine use would need some means of compensating for changing battery voltage. The article by Cole should be consulted for details of such circuits.)

3. If a sensitive millivoltmeter is available, the effect of even small changes in the temperature difference between the junctions of a thermocouple may readily be observed.

4. If a self-balancing recording potentiometer is available, it should be examined, and the potential produced by the thermocouple recorded on it.

CHAPTER 5

ALTERNATING CURRENTS

5.1. NATURE OF AC

If a conductor is caused to cut across a magnetic field, an EMF appears between its ends. This EMF is proportional to the rate at which the field is cut and has a polarity depending on the direction of movement. If now this conductor is attached to the surface of a cylinder which is rotated on its

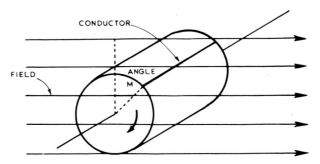

CONDUCTOR

FIELD

ANGLE M

Fig. 5.1. Conductor rotated in magnetic field.

axis in a magnetic field, as shown in Fig. 5.1, the conductor will in one rotation move first down across the field, then back up across it again.

The EMF *induced* will have the form shown in Fig. 5.2,

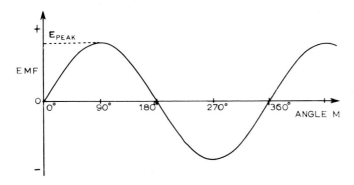

E_{PEAK}

EMF

0°   90°   180°   270°   360°

ANGLE M

FIG. 5.2. Generation of alternating EMF.

which may be expressed by the equation

$$e = E_{peak} \sin M,$$ (5.1)

27

where *e* is the EMF between the ends at any instant, E_{peak} is the maximum EMF and *M* is the angle of rotation of the conductor from the zero position at the top of the cylinder. Each rotation produces one complete *cycle* of alternating EMF. If the cylinder is revolving at *f* revolutions per second, the *frequency* of the EMF is then *f* cycles per second.

We speak of any point in a cycle as a *phase*; thus E_{peak} occurs at the 90° phase. For convenience phase angles are often expressed in *radians* rather than degrees; there are 2π radians in 360°.

If instead of a single conductor, two conductors on opposite sides of the drum are used, it will be seen that the EMFs induced in them will have opposite polarities at any time, since one is always cutting the field in the opposite direction to the other. Thus joining the pair of conductors across the rear of the drum will put their EMFs in series, as shown in Fig. 5.3.

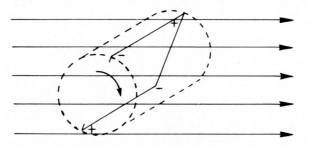

FIG. 5.3. Two rotating conductors in series.

This arrangement may be extended by the use of many conductors, as may be seen by the examination of the generator from an old-style manual telephone or from a bicycle lighting set.

To make this EMF available externally, some arrangement of sliding contacts must be used. A very simple example is seen in the telephone or

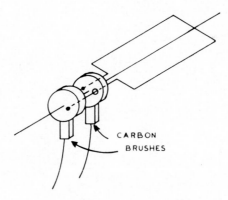

FIG. 5.4. Rotor and slip rings.

bicycle generator, where one contact is made through the bearings of the rotor and the other through a spring contact at the rear. More usually, a pair of *slip rings* is used, as shown in Fig. 5.4.

If a resistive load is connected to the output of such an *alternator*, a current will flow through the circuit. This current will at any instant be directly proportional to the EMF at that instant (Ohm's law), and, consequently, will also be sinusoidal in form.

5.2. AC POWER

Since power dissipated in a resistive load is given at any instant by the product of voltage and current, it will be seen that the *instantaneous* power will reach a peak twice in every cycle. For example, for an AC with a peak voltage of 100 and a peak current of 1 A (through a load of 100 ohm), the power over a cycle will vary as shown in Fig. 5.5.

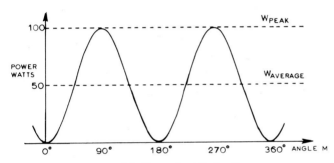

FIG. 5.5. Power in AC circuit.

For most practical purposes the *average* power is of more interest than the instantaneous power, and this is given by

$$W_{av} = \tfrac{1}{2} W_{peak}. \tag{5.2}$$

5.3. RMS VOLTAGE AND CURRENT

To allow the direct calculation of average power, it is usual to specify an AC voltage or current not in terms of its peak value, but in terms of its RMS (*Root Mean Square*) value: this is defined so that RMS voltage multiplied by RMS current gives average power. From the power graph above, it will be seen that at the 45° phase the instantaneous power is equal to the average power. At this phase the voltage and current are both at $1/\sqrt{2} (= 0.707)$ of their peak values, since $\sin 45° = 1/\sqrt{2}$. So we can write

$$E_{RMS} = 0.707 E_{peak} \simeq \tfrac{2}{3} E_{peak} \tag{5.3}$$

or $$E_{peak} = 1.414 E_{RMS} \simeq 1\tfrac{1}{2} E_{RMS}. \tag{5.4}$$

Thus if a supply line is stated to have a voltage of 230, this is an RMS value; the corresponding peak value is 325 V. All wiring must, of course, be insulated adequately to withstand the *peak* voltage.

5.4. MEASUREMENT OF AC

AC voltages and currents are usually measured by converting them to DC and using a moving-coil meter. This process of *rectification* can be done using several circuit configurations, but all employ as their basic element a *semiconductor diode*. This consists of two dissimilar substances placed in contact, and selected so that a current will pass readily from one to the other but will not pass significantly in the opposite direction. Meter rectifiers normally utilise germanium as the basic substance; the underlying principles of the rectifier will be discussed more fully in Chapter 8.

The simplest circuit arrangement is the *half-wave series* rectifier. It is shown in Fig. 5.6 as an AC voltmeter.

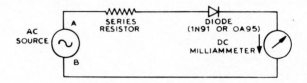

FIG. 5.6. Half-wave series rectifier.

When the EMF from the AC source is at a phase such that A is positive to B, the diode conducts, behaving like a short circuit, and current flows through the meter in the direction of the arrow. When A is negative to B, the diode does not conduct, behaving like an open circuit, and no current

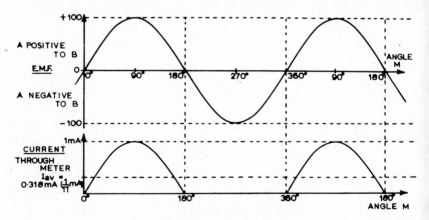

FIG. 5.7. Half-wave rectified current.

flows through the meter. For example, if the AC source has a peak voltage
of 100, and a 0–1 milliammeter and a 100 K series resistor are used, the
situation will be as shown in Fig. 5.7.

The average value of an AC is zero, and unless the frequency is extremely
low, a DC meter simply fails to read it at all, due to the inertia of its moving
parts. The average value of a *half-rectified* wave is found to be $1/\pi$ of its peak
value and, unless the frequency is extremely low, this is the value which the
milliammeter will read.

Half-wave shunt rectification is occasionally found, as shown in Fig. 5.8,
but it is seldom used for metering, because most semiconductor diodes have
unsuitable characteristics.

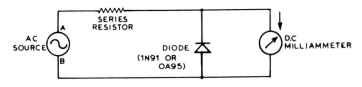

FIG. 5.8. Half-wave shunt rectifier.

When *A* is positive to *B*, the diode does not conduct, and all the current
through the series resistor passes through the meter. When *A* is negative to *B*,
the diode conducts and constitutes a short circuit across the meter. Thus the
current through the meter has the same form as in the previous case.

The *full-wave bridge rectifier*, as shown in Fig. 5.9, is most common.

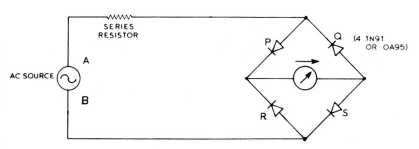

FIG. 5.9. Full-wave bridge rectifier.

When *A* is positive to *B*, current flows from *A* through the series resistor,
P, the meter, S and back to *B*. When *A* is negative to *B*, current flows from *B*
through R, the meter, Q, the series resistor and back to *A*. In each case the
direction of flow through the meter is the same. For example, if the AC
source has a peak voltage of 100, and a 0–1 milliammeter and a 100 K series
resistor are used, the situation will be as shown in Fig. 5.10.

The average value of a *full-rectified* wave is $2/\pi$ of its peak value and again this is the value the meter will read. The advantages of full-wave rectification are obvious: the average value is twice that for a half-wave rectifier, and there will be less pointer vibration for low frequencies, since now two peaks occur in each cycle.

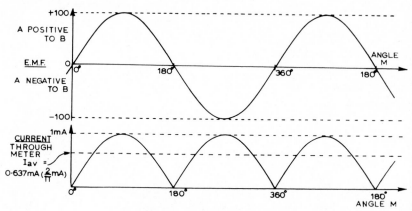

FIG. 5.10. Full-wave rectified current.

Further Reading

ARRL Radio Amateur's Handbook, American Radio Relay League, Concord, 1965.
AGGER, *Alternating Currents* (3rd ed.), Macmillan, London, 1960.

PRACTICAL

Generators (often called magnetos) from old-style manual telephones are still readily available, and form an excellent source of low-frequency AC for experimental purposes. It is best to remove the gear wheels and to attach the driving handle directly to the rotor. An alternative source of AC is the generator from a bicycle lighting set. These are of very similar construction.

1. Examine the construction of the generator to be used and notice the features described in this chapter. Using a 0–1 milliammeter in series with a 100 K resistor, examine the output of the generator as the rotor is turned, slowly at first, and then faster and faster.

2. Set up a 0–1 milliammeter for half-wave series rectification, using a semiconductor diode and 100 K resistor. Notice the reading now as the rotor is turned, slowly at first,

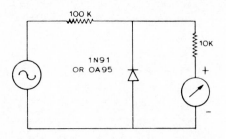

FIG. 5.11. Experimental half-wave shunt rectifier

and then faster and faster. From this reading, calculate the maximum peak voltage you can generate. (Calculate the peak *current* using Fig. 5.7, and then use Ohm's law.) Try the effect of reversing the diode in the circuit.

3. Set up a 0–1 milliammeter for half-wave shunt rectification, using the circuit of Fig. 5.11. (Notice that it is necessary to use a 10 K resistor *in series with the meter*, to allow for the fact that the diode used is not, in fact, a very good short circuit compared with the meter alone.)

4. Set up a 0–1 milliammeter for full-wave bridge rectification, using the circuit of Fig. 5.9, with a 100 K series resistor. Observe the number of output pulses per revolution when the generator rotor is turned slowly. Turn the rotor as fast as possible and use the reading obtained to calculate the peak voltage. (Calculate the peak *current* using Fig. 5.10, and then use Ohm's law.) Compare this value with that obtained in experiment 5.2.

5. If a properly enclosed and safe source of about 6 V AC at supply-line frequency is available, the following experiment may be performed. Using the circuit of experiment 5.4, but substituting 10 K for the series resistor, observe the meter reading when the normal 6 V source is connected. From the reading, calculate the peak voltage, as in experiment 5.4. From the peak voltage, using eqn. (5.3), calculate the RMS voltage. Compare this calculated value with that measured on a commercial multimeter. (In commercial instruments the AC scales are drawn directly in terms of RMS values, although the meter actually indicates $2/\pi$ of peak value of a sine wave, as explained above.)

CHAPTER 6

CAPACITANCE

6.1. STORAGE OF CHARGE

If two metal plates are set up parallel to each other, and in close proximity but not touching, and are connected as shown in Fig. 6.1, pressure on the button will cause a small and transient flow of current in the circuit, as indicated by the two meters. A current will be found to pass from the battery into plate 1, and a similar current will flow from plate 2 back to the battery. This implies that a certain amount of energy has been stored in the arrangement formed by the parallel plates; this arrangement constitutes a *condenser* or *capacitor*. On releasing the button the energy is retained in the condenser, as can be shown by subsequently removing the battery from the circuit, as in Fig. 6.2, and again pressing the button. Current will now be found to flow round the circuit for a short period in the reverse direction, and the stored energy is dissipated as heat in the resistance of the connecting wires.

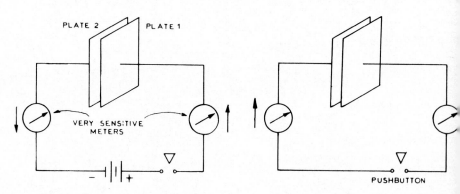

FIG. 6.1. Charging a capacitance.   FIG. 6.2. Discharging a capacitance.

6.2. CAPACITANCE

If instead of reading the current entering or leaving the condenser, the *charge q* entering or leaving is measured (remember that 1 A is 1 coulomb/sec), it is found that the charge stored is directly proportional to the applied voltage. The actual number of coulombs stored per volt applied is defined as the *capacitance* of the condenser, and is measured in *farad*:

$$C = \frac{q}{e}. \tag{6.1}$$

The farad is an impracticably large unit of capacitance, and the microfarad (10^{-6} farad) and picofarad (10^{-12} farad) are the usual units employed.

The capacitance of a condenser can be considerably increased by the insertion of a sheet of solid insulating material between the plates; the material between the plates is called the *dielectric* of the condenser. (In the example of Figs. 6.1 and 6.2 the dielectric is air.) The *dielectric constant* of a material is defined as the factor by which the capacitance of a condenser is multiplied when that material is substituted for a vacuum as the dielectric of the condenser. Typical insulating materials have dielectric constants in the range from 2 to 8.

If condensers are placed in parallel their capacitances are added; this fact is often used to manufacture condensers with multiple interleaved plates, as shown diagrammatically in Fig. 6.3.

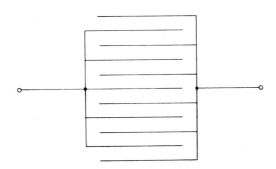

FIG. 6.3. Condenser with multiple plates.

The capacitance of a condenser is directly proportional to the area of the plates and to the dielectric constant of its dielectric, and inversely proportional to the spacing between the plates; it can be shown that

$$C = \frac{0.0884\ ANK}{d}, \tag{6.2}$$

where C is the capacitance in picofarad (pF), A is the area of one plate in square centimetres, N is the number of *dielectrics* in a multiple plate condenser, K is the dielectric constant ($K = 1$ in air) and d is the spacing between the plates in centimetres.

The energy stored in a charged condenser is given by

$$J = \tfrac{1}{2}Ce^2, \tag{6.3}$$

where J is the energy in joules, C is the capacitance in farad and e is the potential difference between the plates in volts. As a rough working rule, an energy of one joule or more is considered potentially lethal.

6.3. CONDENSERS AS USED IN ELECTRONIC EQUIPMENT

An enormous variety of condensers is manufactured, the physical form depending on the purpose for which the condenser is required. A condenser is specified in terms of its capacitance, the peak voltage which it must withstand, and the type of dielectric required; this last factor is governed by the permissible leakage and the rapidity with which the condenser is required to charge and discharge. For details, the manufacturers' literature should be consulted, but Table 6.1 is typical of modern practice. Only the highest quality modern condensers should be used in medical electronic equipment. As for resistors, preferred values are commonly used.

TABLE 6.1.
SELECTION OF CONDENSER TYPES

Capacitance	Nature of dielectric		
	Peak volts up to 50 (typical transistor circuitry)	Peak volts up to 500 (typical valve circuitry)	Peak volts above 500
1 pF 10 100	ceramic	mica / ceramic	mica
0·001 µF 0·01 0·1	ceramic	polyester	oil or oil-im-
1 10 100	electrolytic	electrolytic	pregnated paper
1,000 10,000	electrolytic		

It should be noted that electrolytic condensers are *polarised*; with few exceptions they cannot be used with alternating voltages, and in a direct-voltage circuit must be connected with the end marked positive to the positive supply. They will be rapidly destroyed if this is overlooked.

Variable condensers in the range 1–1000 pF are also available in a wide variety of forms, with either ceramic or air dielectric. Above this range, variability can be obtained only by selection of a range of fixed condensers with a switch.

6.4. CHARGE AND DISCHARGE OF CONDENSER–RESISTOR COMBINATION

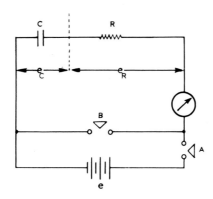

FIG. 6.4. Charge and discharge of RC series combination.

Consider the circuit shown in Fig. 6.4; make $C = 10$ μF, $R = 1$ M, $e = 100$ V, and suppose the condenser is initially discharged. On pressing button A, the condenser commences to charge through the resistor; at any instant the sum of the voltage across the condenser, e_C, and the voltage across the resistor, e_R, must equal e. Initially, the condenser voltage is zero, so the resistor voltage alone must equal e. Thus the initial current will be, by Ohm's law, 100 μA. This is by definition 100 μcoulomb/sec, and $e = q/C$, so e_C will commence to rise at 10 V/sec. However, as e_C rises, e_R must diminish correspondingly. This implies, by Ohm's law, that the current must also diminish, and so must the rate of rise of voltage across the condenser. The charging curve is found to have the form of Fig. 6.5.

Eventually the condenser voltage will reach e, the resistor voltage will be zero and no further current will flow.

It can be shown that the equation to a charging curve of this sort is

$$e_C = e(1 - \varepsilon^{-t/RC}), \tag{6.4}$$

where $\varepsilon = 2.718 \ldots$, the base of natural logarithms.

Table 6.2 gives values of $\varepsilon^{-t/RC}$ and $(1 - \varepsilon^{-t/RC})$ for a range of values of t/RC.

4

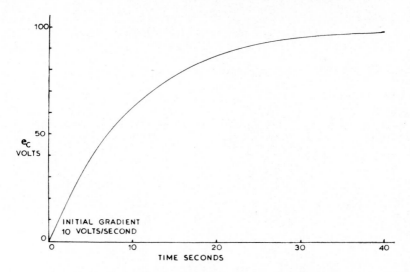

FIG. 6.5. Charging curve for RC series combination.

TABLE 6.2.
VALUE OF EXPONENTIAL TERM IN EQN. (6.4)

t/RC	$\varepsilon^{-t/RC}$	$1 - \varepsilon^{-t/RC}$
0	1·00	0
0·2	0·82	0·18
0·4	0·67	0·33
0·6	0·55	0·45
0·8	0·45	0·55
1·0	0·37	0·63
2·0	0·13	0·87
3·0	0·05	0·95
4·0	0·02	0·98

Once the values of R and C are determined in a particular circuit, the value of t/RC can be calculated for any time t after charging has started. Then, from Table 6.2 and eqn. (6.4), the corresponding value of e_C can be determined.

The term RC is described as the *time constant* of the circuit, since it alone governs the rate at which the condenser voltage approaches its final value. In particular, when $t = RC$ (one time constant) the condenser voltage will always have covered 63% (approximately $\frac{2}{3}$) of its total rise; when $t = 5RC$ (five time constants) the voltage is within 1% of its final value.

If, having charged the condenser fully, the button B is pressed, current will flow out of the condenser through the resistor, rapidly at first, and then slower and slower as the condenser empties. The discharge curve will be as shown in Fig. 6.6 for the values of R, C and e given above.

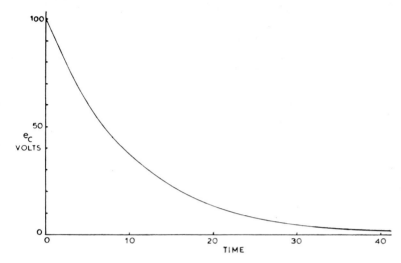

FIG. 6.6. Discharge curve for RC series combination.

The equation to a discharge curve of this sort is

$$e_C = e\,\varepsilon^{-t/RC},\qquad(6.5)$$

so that again 63% of the total voltage change will be traversed in one time constant, and 99% in five.

The importance of this circuit is that it is the basis of nearly all practical timing and time-delay circuits. It will be noticed that the initial portion of both charge and discharge curves is very nearly a straight line; this fact is used when it is desired to approximate a voltage rising or falling linearly with time. Practical applications of the circuit will be discussed later in this book.

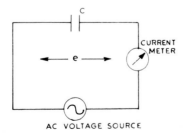

FIG. 6.7. AC applied to a condenser.

6.5. AC APPLIED TO A CONDENSER

If a condenser is connected to a source of alternating voltage of peak value e_{peak}, as in Fig. 6.7, at any instant the condenser voltage must be the same as that of the source. As the source voltage rises, current must flow into one plate and out of the other as the condenser charges. When the voltage is at its peak, the condenser is fully charged, so no current is flowing. As the voltage falls to zero and reverses, current flows out of the condenser, and is actually flowing at its maximum rate as the voltage passes through zero. The condenser then charges up in the reverse direction, the current again dying away as the voltage reaches its maximum reverse value. This process is repeated for each reversal of the applied voltage, so that the meter registers an AC through it. In fact, an AC meter shows a steady value of current, although no electrons ever cross between the plates of the condenser. The magnitude of the AC which flows can be calculated from the equation

$$i = \frac{e}{1/2\pi fC}, \tag{6.6}$$

where i is the current flowing, e is the voltage of the source, f is the frequency in cycles per second and C is the capacitance in farad. i and e can be both peak values, or, more usually, both RMS values.

This equation is very similar to Ohm's law for the current in a resistor,

$$i = \frac{e}{R},$$

where $1/2\pi fC$ is analogous to R. In fact, we speak of $1/2\pi fC$ as the *impedance* of the condenser. Impedance is usually represented by the symbol Z. The impedance is inversely proportional to the capacitance, and also to the frequency, so it is meaningless to state an impedance unless the frequency is stated or implied. The unit of impedance is the ohm, and resistance is, in fact, a variety of impedance; but *the impedance of a series resistor and condenser combination is NOT the arithmetical sum of the individual impedances.*

A useful practical value to memorise is that a condenser of 1 μF has an impedance of 1591 ohm (say 1600 ohm) at 100 c/s. The impedance of any other condenser at any other frequency can then be obtained by inverse proportion.

6.6. MEASUREMENT OF CAPACITANCE

In practice, AC methods are always used to measure capacitance. Some multimeters are provided with one or more capacitance ranges. These operate with an AC source of known voltage and an AC milliammeter exactly as the ohmmeter operates for DC. They are suitable only for condensers of fairly large capacitance, since the AC source is derived from the supply line, with a frequency of 50 or 60 c/s, and at this frequency the impedance of the smaller condensers is very large.

It is more common to use an *AC bridge circuit* for capacitance measurement, as shown in Fig. 6.8. In this circuit an AC source and an AC balance detector are used, and the unknown capacitance is balanced against a standard capacitance.

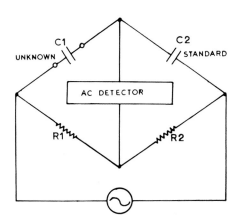

FIG. 6.8. Capacitance bridge.

Balance will be obtained when

$$\frac{C_1}{C_2} = \frac{R_2}{R_1}. \tag{6.7}$$

It should be noted that these methods *cannot be used for electrolytic condensers*, which are normally tested by a measurement of time constant.

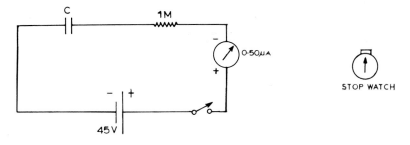

FIG. 6.9. Charging curve experiment.

Further Reading

ARRL Radio Amateur's Handbook, American Radio Relay League, Concord, 1965.

AGGER, *Alternating Currents* (3rd ed.), Macmillan, London, 1960.

Manufacturers' literature on condensers.

PRACTICAL

1. Set up the circuit shown in Fig. 6.9, using for C a combination of polyester or oil-impregnated condensers of at least 10 μF. When ready, close the key and plot the charging current as a function of time. The same curve may be repeated as often as required by switching off, discharging the condenser bank by a short circuit across it and starting again. From your curve, and using Ohm's law, deduce and plot the curve of condenser voltage as a function of time. Deduce from this curve the time constant of the combination: does it agree with the calculated value? Is the condenser block potentially lethal when fully charged? Comment on the validity of the "one joule rule" given at the end of § 6.2.

Repeat the experiment with a different value of C. What would be the effect of varying R instead?

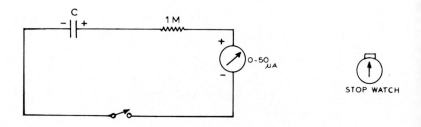

FIG. 6.10. Discharge curve experiment.

2. Set up the circuit shown in Fig. 6.10 using the same value of C as you used originally in experiment 6.1. With the switch open, charge the condenser to 45 V (with the polarity as shown) from your battery and remove it. When ready, close the key and plot the discharge current as a function of time. From the curve, deduce and plot the curve of condenser voltage as a function of time. If time permits, replot the last graph on two decade semi-logarithmic graph paper, using the logarithmic scale for voltage and the linear scale for time, and draw the straight line of best fit through the points. From either of these last two graphs, deduce the time constant of the circuit.

3. Connect a 0–1 DC milliammeter in series with a 100 K resistor, and place the combination across the output of a telephone or bicycle generator. Turn the rotor slowly and steadily, and observe the position of the handle at which the positive and negative peaks of current occur. Now substitute a 0·47 μF condenser for the 100 K resistor, again turn the rotor slowly and steadily, and observe that an AC flows through the condenser. At what positions of the handle do the peaks of current occur now?

4. Set up a capacitance bridge, as shown in Fig. 6.11; the DC milliammeter will indicate any AC caused by the bridge being out of balance. The ratio potentiometer should be provided with a pointer knob and linear scale. Calibrate the bridge by tabulating the balance point on this scale for a number of known capacitances placed in the C_x position, and drawing a calibration graph.

Connect up several parallel condenser combinations, measure their capacitances and compare with the calculated values. Connect two 0·22 μF condensers in series and measure the capacitance of the combination. How can the observed result be obtained by calculation?

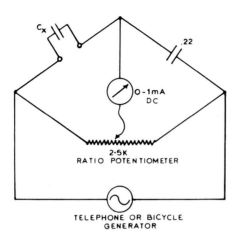

FIG. 6.11. Capacitance bridge experiment.

5. If a cathode-ray oscilloscope with a very slow time base and a long persistent screen is available, observe directly the charge and discharge curves of experiments 6.1 and 6.2, and read off the time constant.

6. Examine any commercial capacitance bridges and condenser-leakage testers which may be available.

CHAPTER 7

INDUCTANCE

7.1. INDUCTANCE

Whenever a current is established in a length of wire, a magnetic field appears about the wire; an increasing current will cause a spreading field, and vice versa. If the length of wire is formed into a coil, and a current established in it, the spreading field about each portion of the wire must cut other portions; this will result in the generation of an EMF in them. It can be shown that this EMF is always in such a direction as to oppose the original rise of current. Similarly, when the current is decreased, the collapsing field generates an EMF in such a direction as to tend to maintain the current.

This effect is known as *inductance* and the coil as an *inductor*. If the current through an inductor is caused to increase at a rate of one ampere per second, and the resulting induced voltage across its terminals is one volt, it is said to have an inductance of one *henry*:

$$e = L\dot{i}, \tag{7.1}$$

where e is the induced EMF in volts, L is the inductance in henries, $\dot{i}$ is the rate of change of current in amperes per second. Conversely, if one volt is applied to the terminals of an inductor of one henry, the current will rise at one ampere/second.

The inductance of a coil can be greatly increased by inserting a core of some suitable magnetic material, since this increases the field due to a given current. The core may consist either of strips of a suitable iron alloy or an iron powder bonded into the desired shape.

7.2. DC APPLIED TO INDUCTOR AND RESISTOR IN SERIES

If a steady voltage is applied to an inductor and resistor in series, and the current observed, it is found to rise in the same way as the condenser voltage does in the RC circuit observed in Chapter 6. In this way the current is given by

$$i = \frac{e}{R} (1 - \varepsilon^{-Rt/L}) \tag{7.2}$$

and the time constant is thus L/R. e/R is the current eventually reached in the circuit, as would be expected from Ohm's law, since after several time constants the current is no longer changing and is limited only by the resistance in the circuit.

If a short circuit is placed across the combination while it is carrying a steady current, the current falls exponentially, just as the condenser voltage did.

An inductor carrying a current is storing energy in its magnetic field, of an amount in joules given by

$$J = \tfrac{1}{2}Li^2. \tag{7.3}$$

If the series circuit is opened suddenly, this energy must be dissipated before the current can stop, and the induced voltage rises suddenly until a spark occurs at the switch contacts.

Even if no external series resistor is used in series with the inductor, all practical inductors have a considerable resistance in their windings which is effectively (and inseparably) in series with their inductance. This must always be taken into account in determining the behaviour of a practical inductor in a circuit.

7.3. AC APPLIED TO AN INDUCTOR

If an alternating voltage is applied to an inductor, an AC will flow through it. It will be seen from the basic definition of the henry that since e is proportional to rate of change of current, the peak of voltage will be reached when the current is changing fastest, which is in fact as it passes through zero. (This is the exact opposite of the situation in a condenser.) The magnitude of the current is given by

$$i = \frac{e}{2\pi fL}, \tag{7.4}$$

where f is the frequency in cycles per second, L is the inductance in henries, and i and e are in RMS amperes and volts respectively. Here $2\pi fL$ is the *impedance* of the inductor and again is measured in ohms. Once again, this impedance cannot be combined arithmetically with resistive or capacitive impedances.

7.4. CALCULATION OF IMPEDANCES IN SERIES

The rules for combination of the three different types of impedance can be shown to be: (i) If both inductive and capacitive impedance are present in series, one counteracts the other. Take the difference between them to get the total impedance, which will be inductive or capacitive, depending on which of the original impedances was the larger. (ii) Combine this with any resistive impedance by adding the two geometrically at right angles to each other, and taking the total impedance as the length of the hypotenuse:

$$Z_{\text{total}} = \sqrt{(Z^2_{\text{resistive}} + Z^2_{\text{inductive or capacitive}})} \qquad (7.5)$$

This rule is illustrated in Fig. 7.1.

$$e = i \cdot Z_{\text{total}}. \qquad (7.6)$$

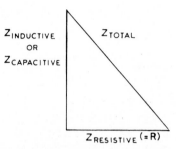

FIG. 7.1. The impedance triangle.

RMS voltage and current in the series circuit are then related in magnitude by the modified form of Ohm's law.

7.5. TRANSFORMER

If two separate coils are interwound, and a varying current flows in one coil (the *primary* coil), the varying magnetic field set up will cut the turns of the second coil (the *secondary* coil), and induce an EMF in it as well as in itself. It will be clear that if both coils have the same number of turns the two induced EMFs must be identical, since they are both produced by the same field cutting identical coils: this is to say that the EMF obtained from the secondary must be equal to the EMF applied to the primary. If the secondary has twice the number of turns, the secondary EMF will be twice that of the primary, and so on. In particular, this rule holds if the EMFs are the peak or RMS values of alternating voltages. Thus a transformer can be used to raise or lower an alternating voltage.

Since there is no source of power within the transformer it would be expected that the output power, neglecting internal losses, would equal the input power. Thus

$$W_{\text{sec}} = W_{\text{pri}},$$
$$E_{\text{sec}} \cdot I_{\text{sec}} = E_{\text{pri}} \cdot I_{\text{pri}} \qquad (7.7)$$

and if, for example, the secondary voltage is twice that of the primary, the primary current is twice that of the secondary.

A further interesting result arising from the foregoing is that there has been an *impedance* transformation. Assume, for example, the transformer of Fig.

7.2, with primary voltage 100 V RMS, secondary voltage 10 V RMS, and primary current 1 A RMS. The transformer ratio is thus 10 : 1, and the secondary current must be 10 A RMS, implying a secondary load of 1 ohm.

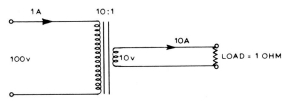

FIG. 7.2. Impedance transformation.

But the load which the primary supply circuit "sees" is, by Ohm's law, $R = E/I = 100/1$ ohm $= 100$ ohm.

A similar argument for the general case of a transformer of turns ratio N shows that the resistance seen will be increased by a factor N^2. Transformers are frequently used for this purpose.

7.6. SATURATION

If an increasing current is passed through the primary of a transformer, the magnetic field will increase correspondingly only up to a definite limit set by the properties of the iron core, which is said to *saturate*. From this point on, any increase is due to the coils alone. There can now be only a slight EMF induced in either the secondary or the primary, since the field is increasing only slowly through each. The secondary output almost disappears and so does the primary induced EMF. This implies that the primary inductance has almost vanished, and current flow is now limited only by the primary resistance. In general, an excessive current will flow and destroy the transformer. Hence a transformer may be used at a voltage or current lower than its rated limits, but overheats rapidly if these are exceeded. Further, since the primary impedance is directly proportional to frequency ($Z = 2\pi f L$), a frequency below the value for which the transformer is designed will produce an excessive primary current even if the rated voltage is used.

Further Reading

ARRL Radio Amateur's Handbook, American Radio Relay League, Concord, 1965.
AGGER, *Alternating Currents* (3rd ed.), Macmillan, London, 1960.
SCROGGIE, *Radio and Electronic Laboratory Handbook* (7th ed.), Iliffe, London, 1961.

PRACTICAL

1. Measure the DC resistance of an iron-cored inductor, using an ohmmeter (a power-supply filter choke is suitable). Assuming the nominal value of inductance marked on the inductor, what is its time constant? (If a current rating is marked on the case this is the maximum DC the inductor can carry without overheating or saturating.) Assuming that a

steady EMF of 6 V is suddenly applied to the terminals, and using Table 6.2, plot a graph of rising current as a function of time.

For any inductor normally used, the time constant is too short to be observed satisfactorily on a moving-coil meter. If a cathode ray oscilloscope is available the circuit of Fig. 7.3 may be set up.

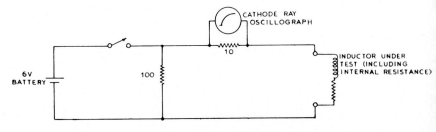

FIG. 7.3. Inductance measuring set.

The oscilloscope is set up to read current by measuring the voltage dropped across the 10 ohm resistor and applying Ohm's law. The 100 ohm resistor has no effect on the behaviour of the inductor when the switch is closed, but provides an energy discharge circuit when the switch is opened. This avoids the production of a very large induced EMF as the inductor current is abruptly reduced to zero. What will be the time constant of *discharge* for your own inductor in this circuit? (Do not forget the added 100 ohm.) Plot the discharge curve, again using Table 6.2. Insert your own inductor in the demonstration circuit, and compare the charge and discharge curves obtained with your calculated curves. Estimate the inductor time constant from the oscilloscope, and from this calculate the true inductance.

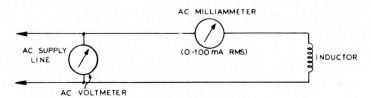

FIG. 7.4. Impedance test set.

2. Connect your inductor in the circuit of Fig. 7.4, using great care not to touch any part of the circuit unless the supply-line connection is *unplugged*.

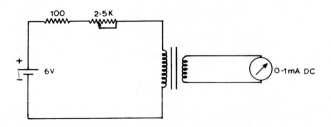

FIG. 7.5. Effect of changing DC in transformer.

Read the voltage and current, and hence calculate the impedance of the inductor at the supply-line frequency. Using this value and the measured resistance, calculate the inductance. How significant is the resistance in determining the total impedance at the supply-line frequency?

3. Set up the circuit of Fig. 7.5, using any small transformer.
Raise and lower the primary current slowly, then more and more rapidly, and observe the magnitude and direction of the induced secondary EMF.

4. A demonstration of a power-transformer test circuit may be set up, using the circuit of Fig. 7.6. A suitable transformer is one converting the supply-line input to 110 V output.

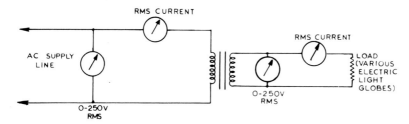

FIG. 7.6. Power transformer test circuit.

For each load used, tabulate the four meter readings, and calculate and tabulate load resistance, power in load, apparent power ($E_{pri} . I_{pri}$) in primary circuit and apparent load as seen looking into primary (E_{pri} / I_{pri}). Notice that with no secondary load, a small primary current (typically 100 mA RMS) is drawn. This is the transformer *magnetising current*.

CHAPTER 8

TRANSISTOR AMPLIFIER

8.1. SEMICONDUCTORS

Semiconductors are materials whose electrical properties lie between those of conductors and those of insulators. Two semiconductor materials are in common use, germanium and silicon. By producing these substances in a very high state of purity, and then suitably "doping" them with a minute trace of impurity, they can be produced in two forms. One is the negative form (*N*-germanium or silicon), in which the impurity gives rise to a supply of free electrons, like those in a metallic conductor. The other is the positive form (*P*-germanium or silicon), which contains a supply of sites deficient in electrons. These "holes" can be caused to move through the material by the application of a potential difference, and in all respects behave as though they were free positive charges.

8.2. PN JUNCTION

A junction formed between a wafer of the *P* form and a wafer of the *N* form constitutes a semiconductor diode. If the *P* layer is made positive to the *N* layer (*forward bias*), holes and electrons move through the layers as shown in Fig. 8.1.

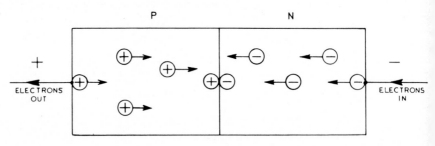

FIG. 8.1. Forward bias at *PN* junction.

At the junction, holes and electrons meet and cancel each other. At the negative terminal, new electrons are continually injected, and at the positive terminal holes are continually injected as electrons are removed. There is

:hus a steady flow of current through the device. On the other hand, if the N ayer is made positive to the P layer (*reverse bias*) holes and electrons move ıs shown in Fig. 8.2.

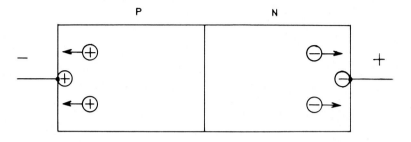

FIG. 8.2. Reverse bias at PN junction.

At the junction, nothing is available to pass a current. At the negative :erminal, holes accumulate (some are cancelled by electrons from the nega- :ive lead when the potential difference is first applied to the device) and at the ɔositive terminal, electrons accumulate (some are removed by the positive ead when the potential difference is first applied). So in an ideal system no :teady current can flow; in actual diodes, the P material always contains a 'ew electrons and the N material a few holes. These *minority carriers* give 'ise to a small reverse leakage current.

8.3. THE TRANSISTOR

A transistor consists of two such PN junctions back to back, to form :ither a PNP or an NPN combination. The three layers are referred to as the :ollector, base and emitter. The collector and emitter, though of the same naterial, differ in physical construction; the base layer is extremely thin. ʌ PNP transistor is represented in Fig. 8.3.

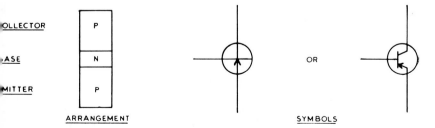

FIG. 8.3. PNP transistor.

For the *NPN* transistor, the arrow is reversed as in Fig. 8.4.

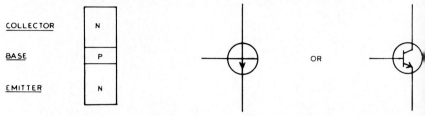

FIG. 8.4. *NPN* transistor.

The *PNP* transistor is operated with collector negative to base, the *NPN* with collector positive to base. *PNP* transistors will be discussed from here on, but it will be understood that their *NPN* counterparts behave in a precisely similar fashion if all polarities are reversed.

In this book, transistors, whether *NPN* or *PNP*, will always be drawn with the collector uppermost, and the direction of current will be taken as from the supply to the collector and from the input to the base. The emitter current is always the sum of the base and collector currents.

Consider a transistor set up as in Fig. 8.5.

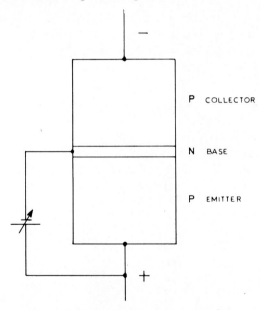

FIG. 8.5. Basic *PNP* transistor connections.

If the base is held positive to the emitter, it will be seen that both *PN* junctions are reverse biased and no current flows across either. However, as soon as the base is made slightly negative to the emitter, the base-to-emitter junction is forward biased and a copious stream of holes from the emitter enters the base. Most of these holes, because of the thinness of the base layer, are not can-celled by the electrons from the base, but enter the collector layer, and pass to the collector terminal, constituting an emitter-to-collector current. The magnitude of this current is controlled by the original base current, which is clearly much smaller than it.

8.4. TRANSISTOR TRANSFER CHARACTERISTIC

Suppose a transistor is set up on the circuit of Fig. 8.6.

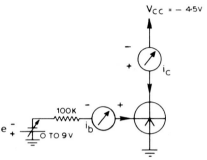

FIG. 8.6. Circuit to measure transfer characteristic.

By varying the voltage e of the battery, a range of values of base current i_b can be obtained. If a tabulation of collector current i_c as a function of base

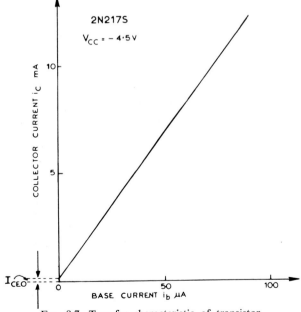

FIG. 8.7. Transfer characteristic of transistor.

current i_b is made, it will be found that i_c is linearly related to i_b. This relation for a typical small germanium transistor is shown in Fig. 8.7; it is known as the *transfer characteristic* of the transistor, since it relates output current to input current.

The straight line does not pass exactly though the origin of the graph; with zero base current (that is, with the base disconnected entirely) a small collector current flows. This *collector leakage current* is usually allotted the symbol I_{CEO}, which is interpreted as "the current from collector to emitter when the base current is zero". (The symbol I_{CO}' is also found.) For a typical small germanium transistor at room temperature it is about 100 μA, and for a silicon transistor much less. It is highly temperature dependent.

The equation to the straight line is

$$i_c = \beta i_b + I_{CEO}, \tag{8.1}$$

where β is the gradient. β (also called h_{fe}) is the *current gain* of the transistor. It is typically in the range 50–150; it varies considerably between individual specimens of transistor.

If the base *voltage* is measured while the collector is drawing current, it will be found to lie between emitter and collector voltages, a fraction of a volt away from that of the emitter.

8.5. TRANSISTOR OUTPUT CHARACTERISTIC

Since collector current depends both on base current and on collector voltage, the properties of the transistor would need to be represented by a

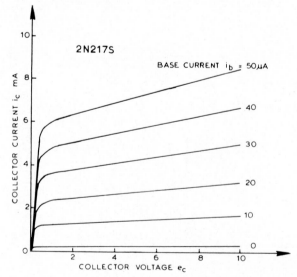

FIG. 8.8. Output characteristic of transistor.

family of transfer curves, each for a different collector voltage. It is more useful, however, to represent the same information by a family of *output* curves, such as those of Fig. 8.8.

Occasionally, a meter or relay in the collector circuit is operated directly by the collector current; often, however, it is desired to produce a change in output voltage proportional to the input current. This is done by the inclusion of a *load resistor* in series with the collector circuit: this by Ohm's law will produce a voltage drop across it proportional to the current through it. However, in doing so, it reduces the effective collector voltage by the same amount. Consider the situation shown in Fig. 8.9.

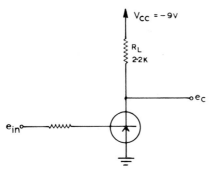

FIG. 8.9. Effect of collector load resistor.

If the transistor is prevented from drawing collector current by the application of a positive voltage at e_{in}, there will be no voltage drop across R_L, and

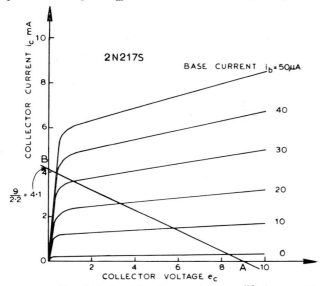

FIG. 8.10. Load line for transistor amplifier.

e_c will be -9 V; this is represented by point A on the graph in Fig. 8.10. If now e_{in} is made sufficiently negative, the transistor will become practically a short circuit from collector to emitter; e_c falls to zero, the full supply voltage appears across R_L, and by Ohm's law the current flowing must be 9/2·2, or 4·1 mA. This is represented by point B. It is easy to see that a straight line drawn between A and B will by Ohm's law give e_c for any other value of i_c; this is the *load line* for a supply voltage of -9 and a collector load of 2·2 K. Following the same argument, the load line for any other value of load resistor and supply voltage can be superimposed on the output characteristic, and the output voltage for any given input current read off.

8.6. TRANSISTOR AMPLIFIER

If it is desired to *amplify* a sinusoidal input, which varies equally above and below a zero base line, it will be necessary to set the transistor initially to operate in the centre of its working range, with its collector at about $-4·5$ V. From the load line of Fig. 8.10, it is seen that an initial base current of 15 μA is required for this; such an initial current is known as *bias current*. This is usually supplied from the same source as the collector current, and the simplest way of doing it is shown in Fig. 8.11. Since the base voltage is always very close to zero, Ohm's law shows that a 560 K resistor returned to the -9 V supply will produce a base current of about 15 μA. The symmetrical input current from the source of signal is then added to or subtracted from this through the condenser C; it can have a peak value of about 12 μA, and this will swing the output voltage by about $\pm$ 3 V.

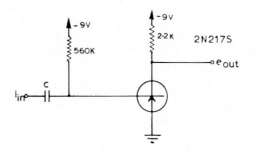

FIG. 8.11. Simple amplifier circuit.

8.7. STABILITY

It is instructive to assemble the circuit of Fig. 8.11 using a germanium transistor, and to examine its operation. Two major defects will at once become apparent. Firstly, it is unlikely that the collector voltage will be resting at $-4·5$ V; it may lie anywhere from almost -9 V, because the specimen of transistor used is not identical with the one for which the curves were drawn. Secondly, even if it is forced to -4.5 V by varying the base resistor to give a suitable value of base current, it will still be quite temperature-sensitive. Warming the transistor gently will at once move it out of its operating range.

To overcome these defects, two modifications are made, to yield the final circuit shown in Fig 8.12.

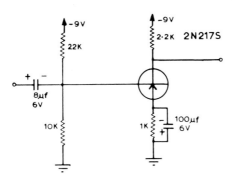

FIG. 8.12. Practical amplifier circuit.

An emitter resistor is inserted; this stabilises the operating point of the collector voltage, irrespective of the specimen of transistor used. A transistor tending to draw an abnormally large collector current merely develops an extra voltage drop across this resistor, so that the bias current is held down, and conversely for a transistor drawing an abnormally small collector current. The voltage developed by the normal transistor is allowed for by increasing the base voltage correspondingly. The emitter resistor also materially improves the temperature stability. By *bypassing* this resistor with a large condenser, the emitter is effectively connected directly to earth for alternating currents, and the amplification of the AC input signal is not affected.

Secondly, the base bias resistor is replaced by a base voltage divider, so that the base voltage is substantially independent of base current. This further stabilises the amplifier against the effect of ambient temperature changes.

8.8. HEAT SINKS

Transistors required to dissipate more than a fraction of a watt of power are usually designed to operate in conjunction with a *heat sink*; this may consist merely of the metal chassis on which the equipment is assembled, or it may be a special sheet or block of metal. The manufacturers' recommendations on this point should always be consulted when setting up a transistor or power rectifier.

8.9. SELECTION OF TRANSISTOR TYPES

A bewildering array of transistor types is offered for sale; it is strongly recommended that any institution using transistors should draw up a "preferred list" of their own, which will be governed primarily by local availability and price. As a guide, it is suggested that one type in each of the classes of Table 8.1 is likely to be needed.

TABLE 8.1.

TRANSISTOR TYPES

(a) Audio frequency amplifier	(i) general purpose germanium *PNP* (ii) low noise germanium *PNP* and silicon *NPN* (iii) general purpose silicon *PNP* (iv) general purpose silicon *NPN*
(b) Power amplifier, voltage regulator	(i) general purpose germanium *PNP* (normal rating about 40 W)
(c) Radio frequency amplifier	(i) silicon *NPN* with a high frequency cut off of several hundred megacycles per second
(d) Switching	(i) medium speed germanium *PNP* (ii) medium speed germanium *NPN*
(e) Semiconductor diodes	(i) general purpose signal and meter rectifier— germanium point contact (ii) power rectifier silicon 100 V PIV 1 A (iii) power rectifier silicon 400 V PIV 500 mA (iv) power rectifier silicon 800 V PIV 500 mA (v) Zener diode reference elements for 6 V, 12 V, 24 V.

There is a general trend towards using silicon *NPN* rather than germanium *PNP* transistors, and it is becoming increasingly likely that a single transistor type may fulfil several functions on this list.

Further Reading

Basic Theory and Application of Transistors, TM11–690, US Army, 1959.
Mullard Reference Manual of Transistor Circuits, London, 1960.
Selected Semiconductor Circuits, MIL-HDBK-215, US Government Printing Office, 1960.
Transistors—Theory and Applications, Philips, London, 1963.
GE Transistor Manual (7th ed.), General Electric, New York, 1964.
Manufacturers' literature on transistors.

PRACTICAL

Warnings. (i) No changes in the wiring of transistor circuits must be made without first disconnecting all batteries.

(ii) A thermal shunt, such as a pair of artery forceps or long-nosed pliers, should always be used when soldering transistor leads.

1. Set up a small general purpose transistor in the circuit shown in Fig. 8.6, and plot its transfer characteristic. What is its I_{CEO} and β under these conditions? (Note that an adequate heat sink will be required for the transistor, even at low collector currents, to prevent a steady drift in collector current as it warms up. A suitable heat sink for a small transistor consists of a piece of aluminium bar of about 1 in. by $\frac{1}{2}$ in. section, and at least 2 in. long, with a hole of diameter very slightly greater than that of the transistor drilled through its centre. The transistor is coated with silicone grease, which is sold in tubes for this purpose, and pushed into the hole with its leads projecting.)

2. Connect up the simple transistor amplifier of Fig. 8.11 and measure the collector voltage. If it is not about 4·5 V, vary the base resistor until it is. Warm the transistor gently by holding a soldering iron *near* it and watch the collector voltage.

3. Insert the 1 K emitter resistor as in Fig. 8.12, omitting the bypass condenser for the time. If necessary, readjust the base resistor to bring the circuit into the operating range, and again test the temperature stability.

4. Install the base voltage divider as in Fig. 8.12, and again test the temperature stability.

5. Install the input coupling and emitter bypass condensers, as in Fig. 8.12. If an audio-signal generator and oscilloscope are available, apply an input signal to the amplifier and observe the output signal at the collector with the oscilloscope; determine the voltage amplification of the amplifier. (Retain this amplifier for use in the practical work of Chapter 20.)

6. If available, a transistor tester should be examined.

FIG. 8.13. Typical small transistor connections.

CHAPTER 9

VALVE AMPLIFIER

9.1. THERMIONIC DIODE

The thermionic diode contains two elements, the *cathode* and the *plate* (or *anode*, in English texts), in a highly evacuated envelope. Most modern valves are *indirectly heated*: the cathode consists of a nickel sleeve coated with a mixture of rare earth oxides to facilitate emission of electrons, and this is heated by a twisted *filament* inside it, but insulated from it. Where economy of cathode heating power is important *directly heated* valves are used; in these the filament is coated directly with the oxide layer and serves as the cathode. On heating the cathode to a dull red heat, electrons are emitted copiously from its surface into the surrounding vacuum. If nothing diverts them, all these will fall back into the cathode surface. At any instant, however, there will always be a cloud of electrons in the space about the heated cathode; this cloud is described as the *space charge*.

Surrounding the cathode and spaced a little distance away from it is the plate; this is usually a more or less cylindrical shell of nickel. If this is made positive to the cathode by the application of an external source of EMF, some of the space-charge electrons will be attracted to it instead of falling back into the cathode, and this flow of electrons constitutes a current. (Owing to the unfortunate early decision to describe a current as though it flowed from a positive to a negative region, we say that the current flows from plate to cathode.) As the plate is made increasingly positive to the cathode, the current increases. If the plate is made negative to the cathode, however, the current stops, since the plate cannot emit electrons. Accordingly, the thermionic diode functions as a rectifier; there is no reverse leakage current such as occurs in the semiconductor diode, but the internal resistance in the forward direction is much higher.

9.2. THE TRIODE

This is formed by the addition to the diode of a third element, the *grid*, which is a mesh of fine wires interposed between cathode and plate. If a flow of electrons from cathode to plate is occurring, its magnitude may be controlled by making the grid increasingly negative to the cathode, by the application of an external voltage, the bias. If the grid is made sufficiently negative, the flow of electrons can be completely cut off by it. The usual range of bias is between this cut-off voltage and zero, and this range is described as the *grid base* of the valve. If the grid ever becomes positive to the cathode, grid and cathode operate as a diode, and the grid actually collects some of the electrons itself, and passes a current. It still controls the electron flow to the plate under these conditions, but its chief virtue is lost; it now requires power to operate it. In the negative range it does not, since it draws no current itself, although controlling considerable current.

9.3. TRANSFER CHARACTERISTIC OF TRIODE

The properties of a triode can be investigated by the use of the circuit of Fig. 9.1; the conventional symbols e_g and i_p for bias and plate current are indicated. As was done for the transistor in Chapter 8, a graph can be drawn to show i_p as a function of e_g. This *transfer characteristic* will appear as in Fig. 9.2 for a typical 12AU7 triode in the circuit shown in Fig. 9.1.

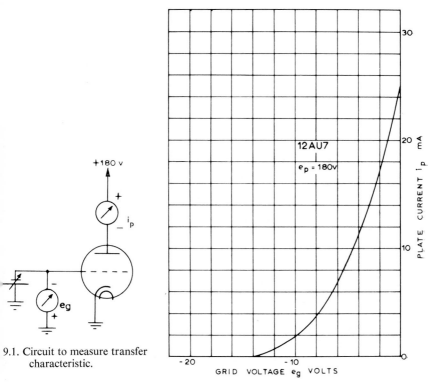

9.1. Circuit to measure transfer characteristic.

Fig. 9.2. Transfer characteristic of triode valve.

The valve is usually operated only on the relatively straight portion of the curve, so in this case the bias would be confined to the range 0 to about -6 V. It will be seen how the grid voltage controls the plate current.

9.4. PLATE CHARACTERISTIC OF TRIODE

Since i_p is a function of both e_g and e_p, a family of curves is needed to express the properties of the valve fully. As in the case of the transistor, the *output* (here the *plate*) characteristic is the most useful. For a 12AU7 this would appear as in Fig. 9.3.

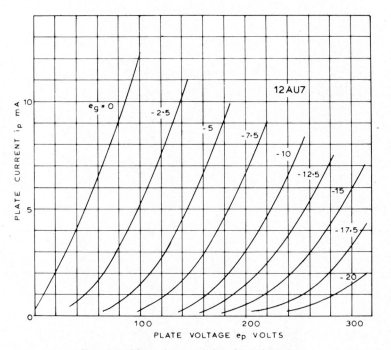

FIG. 9.3. Plate characteristic of triode valve.

Since the valve is usually operated only in a region where the curves are reasonably straight and parallel, its properties may be described by two suitable constants, or *parameters*. In fact, three are normally quoted. The *mutual* or *transfer conductance* (transconductance for short) g_m is the ratio of a small change in i_p to the small change in e_g which produces it, keeping e_p constant. In this case, for e_p held at 100 V, changing e_g from 0 to -2.5 V changes i_p from 12 to 5.2 mA, a ratio of 2.7 mA/V. *The amplification factor* μ is the ratio of a small change in e_p to the corresponding small change in e_g, keeping i_p constant. In this case, for i_p to be held at 10 mA, changing e_g from

0 to $-2 \cdot 5$ V requires e_p to be raised from 86 to 136 V, a ratio of 20. The *plate resistance* r_p is the ratio of a small change in e_p to the small change in i_p which it produces, keeping e_g constant. In this case, for $e_g = 0$ V, raising e_p from 80 to 100 V raises i_p from $9 \cdot 3$ to 12 mA, a ratio of $7 \cdot 4$ K.

These three parameters are related:

$$\mu = g_m \cdot r_p. \tag{9.1}$$

Triodes are generally classified into low μ (about 20), medium μ (about 50), and high μ (about 100) types, each with its own applications. Two triodes are usually included in the one glass envelope.

As for the transistor, a voltage output may be obtained by the insertion of a *plate load resistor* in the plate circuit, and the effect of this may be predicted in the same fashion by the construction of a load line on the plate characteristic. Fig. 9.4 shows a load line drawn for a plate load of 100 K and a supply voltage of 180 on a 12AU7 characteristic.

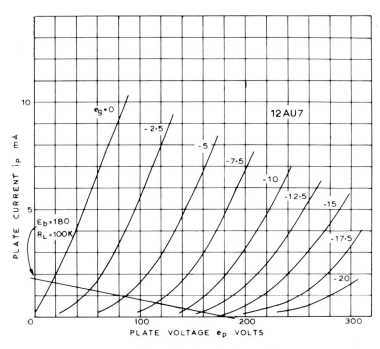

FIG. 9.4. Load line for triode amplifier.

9.5. VALVE AMPLIFIER

To use the valve to amplify an input signal, e_g is caused to vary. From the graph in Fig. 9.4, the value of e_p corresponding to any e_g can be read off. To avoid a flow of grid current, the grid must never become positive; in practice it must remain below about -1 V. To avoid distortion of the signal it must never be carried far negative, into the region where the grid-voltage lines are no longer evenly spaced along the load line. So if a sinusoidal signal is to be amplified, a *bias voltage* must first be placed on the grid, and the signal must then be added to it. (Compare this with the transistor bias current.) The usual arrangement for doing this is shown in the circuit of Fig. 9.5.

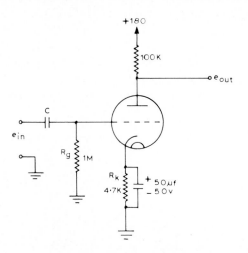

FIG. 9.5. Triode amplifier.

The plate current flows through R_k (*the cathode resistor*), and produces a voltage drop in it, so that the cathode is held steadily positive to earth. The grid is returned to earth through R_g (*the grid leak*), and since no current flows to the grid, is thus at earth. Therefore, *with respect to the cathode*, the grid is negative by the voltage drop across the cathode resistor. Knowing the desired steady plate current and bias for a particular valve type from the valve data book, Ohm's law gives the correct value of R_k to use. The input signal is applied to the grid through a coupling condenser C, whose impedance at the lowest desired frequency must be much less that that of R_g. The *cathode bypass condenser* is required to prevent the voltage drop across R_k varying appreciably as the plate current swings due to the input signal. For use with audio frequencies (say 50 c/s to 20 kc/s), C would be typically 0·047 μF, R_g 1 M and R_k 4·7 K.

If the valve is required to amplify slowly varying signals, such as those from an ECG or EEG, both C and the cathode bypass condenser must be made correspondingly larger. In general the time constant $R_g C$ must be at least ten times the duration of the longest pulse to be amplified, and it is undesirable to increase R_g above about 4·7 M.

This arrangement should be carefully compared with that for the transistor amplifier. Here the bias produced by the cathode resistor is desired; in the case of the transistor amplifier, the voltage drop in the emitter resistor is undesired, and has to be counterbalanced by voltage introduced at the base.

Examination of the load line of Fig. 9.4 shows that this circuit will settle down with a plate current of 1 mA, a plate voltage of 80 V, and a bias voltage of −4·7 V. A swing of 2·5 V at the grid gives a swing of 34 V at the plate, which is a *voltage gain* or *voltage amplification A* of 13·6. It can be shown that the theoretical gain of such an amplifier is given by

$$A = \frac{\mu R_L}{r_p + R_L}. \tag{9.2}$$

If a further stage of amplification is required, the output of this stage may be connected directly to the input coupling condenser of the following stage, as in Fig. 9.6. When the circuit is switched on, this condenser will charge to 80 V, and thereafter only the variations in plate voltage will be transmitted to the following stage.

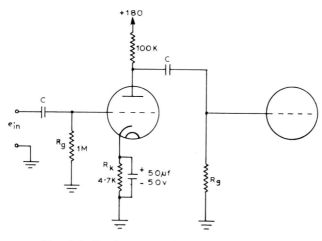

FIG. 9.6. Condenser coupling to following stage.

For a slowly varying signal, it is possible to *direct couple* the following stage, as is done in Fig. 9.7.

Values of R1 and R2 are selected so that when no signal is applied, they form a voltage divider between the steady voltage of the first plate and the negative voltage supply, such that the correct bias is applied to the second stage. Since any slow variations in supply voltages or component values will be amplified by the second stage, extreme stability in supply voltages (including the first-stage filament supply) and components is necessary if direct coupling is used. Notice also that the signal supplied from the first stage is reduced by the voltage divider; in Fig. 9.7 it would be halved.

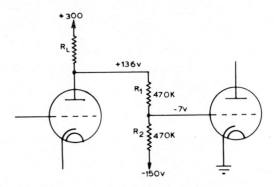

Fig. 9.7. Direct coupling to following stage.

9.6. PENTODES

By the insertion of a second grid (*the screen*) between the plate and grid of a triode, a *tetrode* is formed. The screen is connected to a steady positive supply voltage, usually about half the plate supply voltage. This means that the screen will intercept some electrons which would otherwise have reached the plate; but the remainder are accelerated on towards the plate by it. In fact the *screen voltage* controls the plate current, but the *plate voltage* does not; the plate now receives all those electrons which pass the screen, without being able to control their number. This by definition implies a very high (of the order of thousands) since the grid voltage is very much more effective in controlling plate current than the plate voltage is. Voltage gains of 200 or more can be obtained in this way.

However, the tetrode has a serious basic defect which renders it highly unsatisfactory. Without going into details, this may be corrected by the use of a third grid, the *suppressor*, between screen and plate. This is usually connected to the cathode. Pentodes are used in exactly the same fashion as triodes and numerous examples will be encountered later in the book.

9.7. SELECTION OF VALVE TYPES

As for transistor types, the establishment of a "preferred list" of valves is recommended for any organisation. This list can be relatively short, since valves will be used only where transistors are unsuitable. Table 9.1 may serve as an outline: since valves are far more standardised than transistors, a type number has been suggested in each class.

TABLE 9.1.

VALVE TYPES

(a) Diodes	(i) EHT rectifier, miniature	6X2
(b) Triodes	(i) Low μ twin triode (ii) High μ twin triode	12AU7 12AX7
(c) Pentodes	(i) Low noise audio amplifier (ii) Power output (iii) Series regulator in power supply	EF86 6BQ5 6CW5
(d) Voltage reference tubes	(i) 85 V reference tube (ii) 150 V regulator tube	85A2 OA2

Further Reading

ARRL Radio Amateur's Handbook, American Radio Relay League, Concord, 1965.
TERMAN, *Electronic and Radio Engineering* (4th ed.), McGraw-Hill, New York, 1955.
RCA Receiving Tube Manual, Radio Corporation of America, New Jersey, 1964.

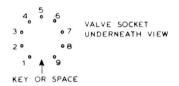

FIG. 9.8. Valve pin numbering.

PRACTICAL

1. Set up the circuit of Fig. 9.9 and use it to plot the transfer characteristic of one triode of a 12AU7 low μ twin triode. Obtain the plate and grid supplies from batteries, and the filament supply from a transformer.

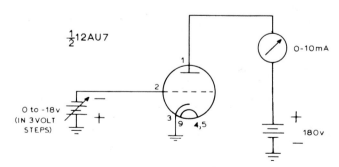

FIG. 9.9. Circuit to measure transfer characteristic.

2. Using the same circuit, plot a family of plate characteristics by varying the plate supply voltage for fixed values of e_g. From the most nearly straight and parallel region of your family of curves deduce the g_m, μ and r_p. Compare these and your curves with those given in the notes for an average 12AU7. How much do they differ, and why?

3. Draw the load line for an amplifier using a 100 K plate load and a supply voltage of 180. Modify your circuit to that shown in Fig. 9.10 and verify that the load line and curves do, in fact, give the relation between input and output voltages. Measure the gain by varying the grid 1·5 V and observing the plate voltage variation. Calculate the gain expected, using the eqn. (9.2).

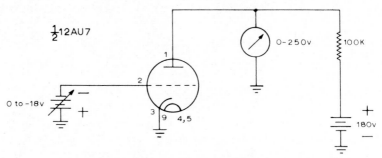

FIG. 9.10. Simple amplifier circuit.

4. If an audio-signal generator and oscilloscope are available, use the amplifier circuit constructed in the practical work of Chapter 1 to set up the arrangement of Fig. 9.11.

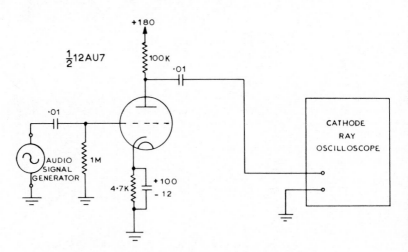

FIG. 9.11. Practical amplifier circuit.

Measure the AC gain of the amplifier. Remove the signal generator and oscilloscope, and measure the DC voltage with respect to earth at cathode, grid and plate. Deduce the plate current.

5. If available, a modern valve-characteristic test set should be examined.

CHAPTER 10

POWER SUPPLIES

10.1. TYPES OF RECTIFIER CIRCUIT

At present (1965) a rapid transition is occurring from valve rectifier to semiconductor rectifier circuits. Although the basic circuit configurations used are identical, the semiconductor rectifier is so superior in performance that it may be regarded as standard in new design, although much commercial equipment in production still uses valve rectifiers.

Four types of circuit are in common use, as shown in Fig. 10.1.

In each of these circuits, R_s represents the total internal resistance of the power transformer. In power supplies for valve circuits, E is typically between 100 and 350 V RMS, depending on the output voltage required, and the condenser C is electrolytic, ranging from 10 to 200 μF, and rated to withstand the peak voltage required. For transistor power supplies E is about 10–50 V RMS, as required, and C will be electrolytic, of about 2000 μF per ampere of load current, and of suitable peak-voltage rating.

Circuit A should appeal to those with a physiological background, since it is the exact analogue of the left ventricle (the transformer), the aortic valve (the rectifier), the great arteries (the capacitance), and the peripheral resistance (the load). The waveforms which occur in this circuit when delivering current into a load are shown in Fig. 10.2.

The rectifier conducts only when the rising transformer voltage on one side of the rectifier exceeds the falling condenser voltage on the other, and so rectifier and transformer current flow only for a short portion of each cycle (compare with cardiac output). During the rest of the cycle, the whole of the load current is supplied by the condenser alone (just as the peripheral circulation is by the elasticity of the walls of the great arteries). The percentage ripple (the pulse pressure) is governed by the load, since if the load current is large, a given capacitance will discharge more before the next pulse of charging current passes through the diode.

At a phase 180° past the conducting peak the condenser is still charged almost to the peak transformer voltage, but the transformer voltage has reversed. For a transformer of peak voltage 200, the situation will now be as in Fig. 10.3.

It will be seen that at this instant the rectifier has across it 400 V trying to make it conduct backwards; this is the *peak inverse voltage* which the rectifier

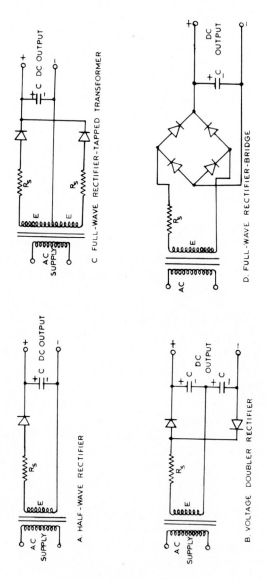

FIG. 10.1. Rectifier circuits.

must withstand. It is clearly approximately equal to twice the transformer peak voltage, or three times its RMS voltage.

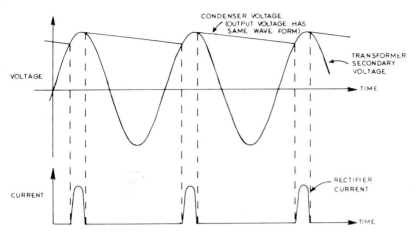

FIG. 10.2. Voltages and currents in half-wave rectifier.

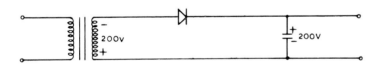

FIG. 10.3. Peak inverse voltage.

The *peak current* which the rectifier passes must be many times the fairly steady output current delivered by the circuit. This is governed by R_s, which must be large enough to keep the peak current within the ratings of the rectifier, but not much larger. (R_s also serves to limit the much more severe *initial surge* when the AC supply line is switched on with the condenser entirely empty.)

The polarity of the output voltage can be reversed by reversing the diode (requiring the condenser to be reversed also, of course); this uses the negative rather than the positive half-cycles from the transformer to charge the condenser. By combining positive and negative half-wave rectification, circuit *B* is obtained. The upper condenser is charged to the peak of *E* in a circuit identical with circuit *A*, and the lower condenser to the peak of *E* by circuit *A* reversed to give negative half-wave rectification. Since both condensers are in series, their voltages add, and the transformer peak current charges them alternately, flowing twice in each cycle. This circuit is the most commonly used of the four in supplies for valve circuits, and is recommended.

Circuit C is found almost universally when valve rectifiers are used; the two diodes are usually built into the one glass envelope. It is also common in low-voltage supplies, using silicon diodes. It is effectively two circuits A connected to the one condenser, and phased so that they charge the condenser alternately in successive half-cycles; the ripple is consequently halved.

Circuit D is the bridge rectifier already considered as a meter rectifier. Its main merits are that it uses only one transformer winding (unlike C) and one condenser (unlike B), and that in each half-cycle the peak inverse voltage is shared by two rectifiers in series. However, as rectifiers are fairly expensive, it is usually avoided except when quite high output voltages or currents are required.

10.2. FILTERING

For nearly all purposes, the ripple obtained from the circuits discussed above is excessive, having a peak-to-peak value of several volts at the working load current. This may be reduced as required by the use of additional filtering, usually consisting of a resistor and condenser in the output lead, as is shown in Fig. 10.4 for a half-wave supply.

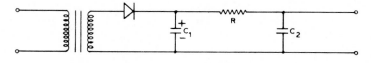

FIG. 10.4. RC filtering.

Here C1 is the original condenser, and R and C2 provide the additional filtering. C2 must now supply the load current directly, and maintain its charge through R. Remembering that C2 has a large capacitance, it will have quite a low impedance at the ripple frequency, and will form a voltage divider with R for the ripple, but not, of course, for DC. Since the ripple is not a pure sine wave, calculation of ripple reduction is quite difficult, and, in fact, design is generally done by the use of families of curves published in most of the references cited.

In many cases several circuits must be supplied from the one power supply. Since usually each circuit draws a fluctuating current as it operates, it is general practice to use not one large resistance–capacitance filter, but a smaller one in each separate supply lead. This serves both to reduce the ripple and to prevent interaction between the individual circuits; they are said to be *decoupled* by this means.

In older valve-rectifier circuits and in large power supplies the filter may consist of an inductor–capacitor combination, as in Fig. 10.5.

Rather better filtering is obtained by this means, and the voltage drop in the resistive filter is avoided, but inductors are bulky, heavy and expensive.

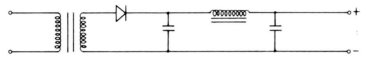

FIG. 10.5. LC filtering.

10.3. GRAPHICAL REPRESENTATION OF POWER-SUPPLY PERFORMANCE

The performance of a rectifier and filter circuit is best described graphically, by a set of three regulation curves drawn for supply voltage maximum, average and minimum, perhaps with typical peak-to-peak ripple voltages written in at a few critical points. (An example is given in Fig. 10.6.)

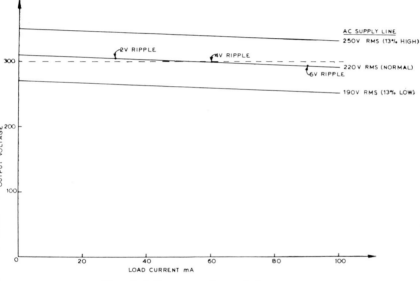

FIG. 10.6. Power supply regulation curves.

Notice that although the nominal AC line voltage for which this equipment is designed is 230, the supply is more likely to be low than high. Accordingly, the mean line voltage is taken as 220, and variations of $\pm 13\%$ give 250 and 190.)

Further Reading

LANGFORD SMITH, *Radiotron Designer's Handbook* (4th ed.), pt 5, AWA, Sydney, 1952.
TERMAN, *Electronic and Radio Engineering* (4th ed.), McGraw-Hill, New York, 1955.
STRAUSS, *Wave Generation and Shaping*, McGraw-Hill, New York, 1961.
Selected Semiconductor Circuits, MIL-HDBK-215, US Government Printing Office, 1960.

PRACTICAL

The construction of a regulated power supply to deliver $+300$ V at 120 mA and -150 V at 20 mA is the first major project in the course. Figure 10.7 shows upper and lower views

(a)

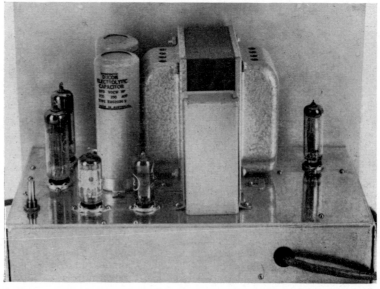

(b)

of the finished supply. It will be used subsequently to supply the oscilloscope to be constructed, and for a number of other experiments.

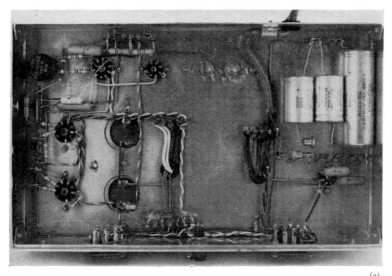

(c)

FIG. 10.7. Regulated power supply. (a) Front. (b) Upper. (c) Lower views.

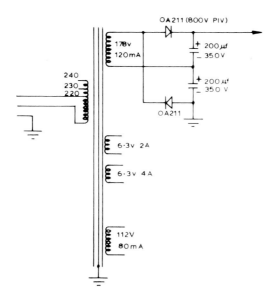

FIG. 10.8. Positive unregulated supply.

1. Commence construction of the power supply by wiring up the positive supply rectifiers and condensers, as shown in Fig. 10.8. Any suitable semiconductor diodes rated at 800 peak inverse volts may be used. Temporarily connect a voltmeter across the output, and a milliammeter in series with a dummy load, also across the output. Plug a Variac (a continuously variable transformer) into the AC supply, and attach an AC voltmeter to read its output. Set it at 220 V and plug the power supply into it. Plot the regulation curve of the power supply for a load current range from 0 to 100 mA, checking that the supply voltage is correct before each reading. If time is available, repeat for supply voltages of 190 and 250.

THIS CIRCUIT IS POTENTIALLY LETHAL.

2. Voltage and current waveforms in a half-wave rectifier power supply should be examined if a cathode ray oscilloscope is available.

CHAPTER 11

REGULATED POWER SUPPLIES

11.1. REGULATION

For many purposes the DC output voltage of a power supply is required to remain constant, despite either slow changes or surges in the AC supply voltage. For satisfactory operation of equipment in areas where supply variations are common (and this includes most hospitals and research establishments), the power supply must be designed for a variation of at least $\pm10\%$ in AC line voltage.

In addition, most equipment imposes a varying load on its power supply, and constancy of voltage in these circumstances is also desirable. Semi-conductor rectifier circuits are at least twice as good as their valve counter-parts in this regard.

A considerable improvement in performance of the power supply under varying AC line voltage can be brought about by the use of a *constant-voltage transformer* inserted in the supply to the rectifier transformer. Most of these produce some distortion of the AC waveform supplied to the rectifier transformer, but this is usually unimportant. The $\pm10\%$ variation can be reduced to $\pm1\%$ or even better by this means, but, of course, there will be no improvement in the performance of the power supply under a varying load current, and no reduction of the output ripple.

The best procedure nearly always is to use some form of *electronic regulation* of the output voltage. The four types which can be recommended are (i) *voltage regulator (VR) tube regulation* for supplies in the range 75–450 V DC at load currents up to about 20 mA, where moderately good regulation is acceptable, (ii) *series valve regulation* for the range 80–450 V DC at any current, where very good regulation is necessary, (iii) *Zener diode regulation* for the range 3–200 V DC at load currents up to about 3 A where moderately good regulation is acceptable, (iv) *series transistor regulation* for the range 3–100 V DC at any load current, where very good regulation is necessary. EHT (extra high tension) supplies will be considered separately in Chapter 12.

11.2. VR TUBE REGULATION

A VR tube contains two electrodes, a large cylindrical cathode and a small rod anode at its centre, and is filled with a rare gas at carefully controlled reduced pressure. If a sufficient voltage is applied across it, a gas discharge forms between the anode and cathode, giving a luminous ionised region over the cathode surface. Once this is formed, the voltage across the tube falls to a definite value, which remains fairly constant, irrespective of the current passing, unless sufficient current is passed to cover the whole cathode surface with the ionised region, or the current is reduced below the minimum value at which ionisation can be maintained. The tube must always be used with a series current limiting resistor, as shown in Fig. 11.1.

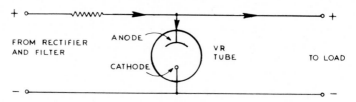

FIG. 11.1. VR tube regulator.

The resistor is selected to allow the VR tube to pass its full rated current at maximum AC line voltage to the power transformer in the absence of a load, and will generally be required to dissipate several watts. As an increasing load current is drawn, current is diverted progressively to the load from the VR tube. Over the full range of current the tube voltage will generally vary by about 5 V. VR tubes may be put in series for higher voltages, but cannot be operated in parallel for higher currents.

Certain types, notably the 85A2 (OG3), are very carefully designed for voltage constancy over many thousand hours, but will handle only a few milliamperes. They are intended as voltage reference tubes and, if operated at constant current, are extremely stable.

11.3. SERIES VALVE REGULATION

The series valve regulator is very versatile, and is extremely effective in maintaining a constant output despite wide supply and load variations, and in reducing ripple. The principle of a typical circuit may be understood by reference to Figs. 11.2 to 11.5. In Fig. 11.2 it is easy to see that a human

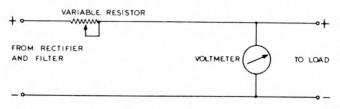

FIG. 11.2. Manual series regulator.

operator can hold the output voltage of the regulator constant by observing the voltmeter, and adjusting the variable resistor in such a direction as to correct variations in output voltage.

In Fig. 11.3 the same arrangement is shown, with a triode valve substituted for the variable resistor; its effective series resistance is controlled by varying its bias manually, and so correcting output voltage variations as before.

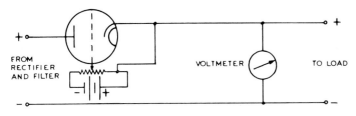

FIG. 11.3. Valve controlled manual series regulator.

Since deviations of the voltmeter from the desired reading tell the operator that a readjustment is necessary, a device to detect deviations would be useful. This may be done as in Fig. 11.4.

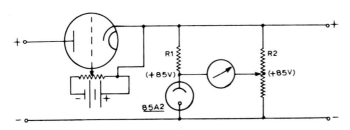

FIG. 11.4. Voltage deviation sensing circuit.

An 85A2 voltage reference tube is maintained in operation by the current through R1. By setting the potentiometer R2 suitably, its wiper can be put at 85 V when the output voltage is at the desired value, and the voltmeter will now read zero. Should the output voltage vary, the meter will immediately deviate from zero, and a manual correction to the bias may be made as before.

The whole system may be rendered automatic by inserting a circuit such that a deviation from zero will cause immediate readjustment of the bias in the appropriate fashion. This can be done by the use of an additional valve, as in Fig. 11.5.

Since this valve has its cathode connected to the constant 85 V, and its grid to the wiper of the potentiometer, a rise in the output voltage of the system will produce a proportional rise in grid voltage. The plate current will rise and this will produce a fall in plate voltage, due to the presence of the plate load resistor R3. However, this plate voltage in turn supplies the bias of the series valve, so a fall here will increase the plate resistance of the series valve, and hence reduce the output voltage.

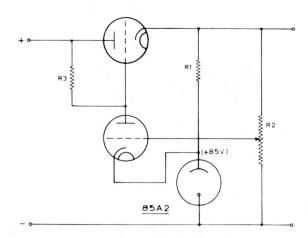

FIG. 11.5. Basic automatic series regulator.

A practical circuit of a series regulator is shown in Fig. 11.6. This has been modified from the basic circuit by the use of a pentode comparison valve to give greater sensitivity in detecting deviations in output voltage. Its screen is fed partly from the regulated output voltage, and partly from the unregulated input voltage; this gives additional sensitivity to supply voltage fluctuations. An output condenser has been added to filter any very

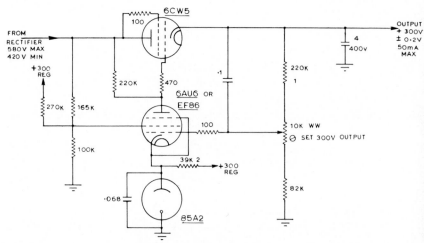

FIG. 11.6. Practical series regulator.

fast pulses which may be generated in the load; a 0·1 μF condenser direct to the grid of the pentode considerably reduces the amount of ripple at the output. A 6CW5 pentode connected as a triode (by joining the screen to the plate by way of a small resistor) is used as the series tube; this gives a regulator considerably superior in performance to one using any type of actual triode at present available.

11.4. ZENER DIODE REGULATION

If a voltage is applied in the reverse direction to a suitably designed semiconductor diode, it will break down at a peak inverse voltage which is remarkably constant, and maintain this voltage across itself over a wide range of currents. Although the mechanism is entirely different, this is the same type of behaviour as is shown by a VR tube, and can be used in the same way. A typical circuit is shown in Fig. 11.7.

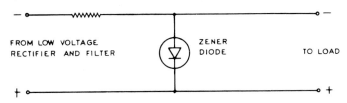

FIG. 11.7. Zener diode regulator.

Such diodes are readily available in the range 3–200 V, and this range is being extended upwards as time goes on. Like VR tubes, they can be connected in series to extend the voltage range, but cannot be connected in parallel.

Strictly speaking, two phenomena of semiconductors are involved. In low voltage diodes the *Zener* effect alone is involved, and this has a marked negative temperature coefficient of voltage. As diodes of progressively higher voltage are considered the *avalanche* effect is involved more and more and the Zener effect less and less. The avalanche effect shows a positive temperature coefficient of voltage, so it will be plain that diodes of a suitable working voltage (in practice, about 5·6 V) will exhibit a nice compromise between the two effects, and will be temperature independent. These are to be preferred wherever the highest stability is required.

11.5. SERIES TRANSISTOR REGULATION

Transistor circuits identical in principle to those of the series valve regulator are frequently used. These, if properly designed, are extremely effective, but usually require more complex circuitry than their valve counterparts to overcome the drifts caused by temperature changes in the transistors. For many purposes a simpler circuit, such as the one of Fig. 11.8, gives adequate regulation.

In this circuit the Zener diode holds the base of the OC29 power transistor at an almost constant voltage. Since the emitter voltage will always remain approximately equal to the base voltage (within a fraction of a volt) the emitter voltage is also held almost constant.

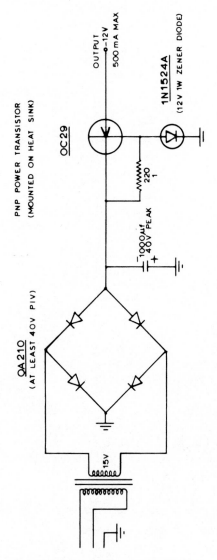

FIG. 11.8. Transistor series regulator.

Regulators of this type are fully discussed by Deichen, in the reference listed at the end of this chapter.

Composite Zener diode elements, having temperature coefficients as low as 0·005 per cent per degree Centigrade, are now available for use as voltage reference units.

Further Reading

MIT Radiation Laboratory Series, vol. 21, chs. 15 and 16, McGraw-Hill, New York, 1948.
Preferred Circuits, NAVWEPS 16-1-519 (2 vols, and supplements), US National Bureau of Standards, 1960.
Selected Semiconductor Circuits, MIL-HDBK-215, US Government Printing Office, 1960.
DEICHEN, *Electronic Engineering*, **31**, 688 (1959).

PRACTICAL

Two sessions will be required for this work; try to complete sections 1 and 2 on the first day.

1. Wire up the negative supply, following Figs. 11.9 and 10.7. Carefully note the polarity of the condensers. Switch on and check that the OA2 regulator valve strikes, and that the output voltage is correct. What current is the OA2 drawing? Unplug, and *discharge all condensers*, in both positive and negative supplies, before proceeding.

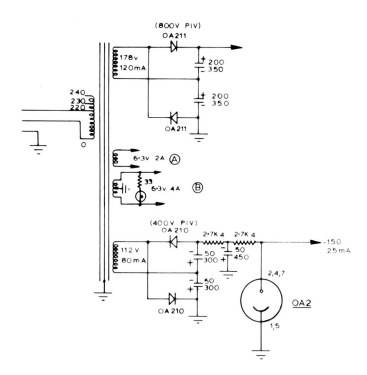

FIG. 11.9. Negative regulated supply.

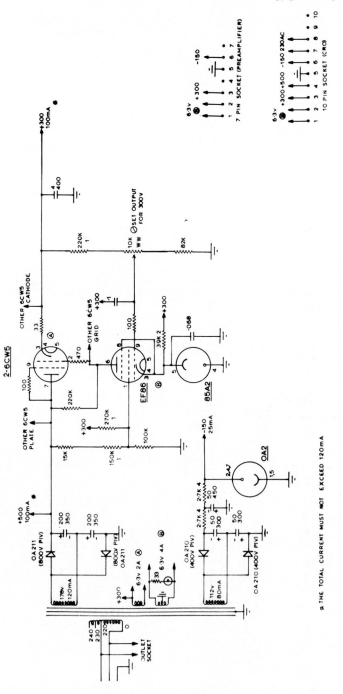

Fig. 11.10. Complete regulated power supply.

2. Install the filament wiring for all the valves of Fig. 11.10, including the pilot lamp. Check that all filaments light when the unit is plugged in. Unplug, and *discharge all condensers*.

3. Install the remainder of the wiring, following the complete circuit of Fig. 11.10, and check it carefully. Connect a voltmeter to the positive output, plug in, and observe the output voltage after the valves have warmed up. Set it to 300 V exactly by the internal control. Using a Variac, milliammeter and dummy load as before, carry out a regulation test on the output from the regulator.

Carry out a measurement of output ripple, for various load currents, using a cathode ray oscilloscope.

N.B. ALWAYS DISCHARGE ALL CONDENSERS BEFORE HANDLING A POWER SUPPLY.

CHAPTER 12

CATHODE RAY TUBE

12.1. THE CATHODE RAY TUBE

A typical cathode ray tube is shown in Fig. 12.1. It comprises (i) the electron gun assembly, which forms a thin beam of electrons focused on the fluorescent screen, and (ii) the two pairs of deflection plates, which deflec the beam horizontally and vertically respectively.

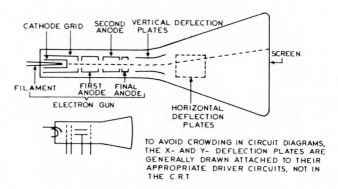

FIG. 12.1. Typical CRT structure and symbol.

The electron gun consists of several parts. (i) The *cathode*, which is the source of the electron stream, is a small nickel cylinder coated with rare earth oxides. It is heated to dull red heat by the filament inside it. (ii) The *grid*, which is so called by analogy with the corresponding part of an ordinary radio valve, is in fact an outer cylinder about the cathode. It is pierced at it end with a small hole on the axis of the tube, to emit a stream of electrons By making the grid more or less negative to the cathode, the intensity of thi stream can be controlled. (iii) Each *anode* is a hollow cylinder with an axia hole through it. The diagram shows a three-anode tube, but two-anode tube are also commonly used. In either case, the first anode is made considerably positive to the cathode, so attracting the electron stream, which passe through it and leaves at considerable velocity. If a second anode is used, it i more negative than the first, but not enough to retard the electron beam much However, it does form an electrostatic "lens" between it and the first anod the focal length of this lens can be varied by altering its voltage. By suitabl adjustment the electron beam can be brought to a focus in the plane of the fluorescent screen. The final anode again is at a high voltage, and accelerates the electrons further, so that they leave it in the form of a thin high-velocity pencil. A two-anode tube omits the second anode in this arrangement, and focusing is done between first and final anode.

The beam then passes between the first pair of deflection plates. If an EMF is applied between these, the beam is repelled from the more negative and attracted to the more positive one, so that its course is changed in proportion to the EMF applied, and the spot it produces on the screen is moved along a line at right angles to the pair of plates. The beam then passes between the second pair, which are at right angles to the first, and this enables the spot to be deflected along a line at right angles to the first one.

The whole CRT is enclosed in a highly evacuated glass envelope and *must be handled carefully*. Dropping, subjecting the glass to sharp knocks, or scratching or straining the envelope may result in fracture and a very nasty explosion, producing a great deal of high-velocity flying glass.

The fluorescent screen is coated with a material which produces a visible spot of light when struck by an electron beam. *Phosphors* used vary, depending on the purpose for which the tube is required. The commonest are:

P1, P31 Green trace, persisting for about 15 msec after the beam is removed. Used for visual observation of medium speed phenomena.

P2 Green-grey trace, persisting for about 2 sec after the beam is removed. Used for visual observation of slow phenomena.

P7 Blue trace with yellow afterglow, which persists for about 10 sec after the beam is removed. Used for visual observation of slow phenomena. This phosphor is very good, but is *very easily burned* by a stationary bright spot.

P11 Blue trace, persisting only for about 5 μsec. This is highly actinic and is used for photographic recording.

12.2. CRT CIRCUITS

It is usual to operate a CRT with the deflection plates at potentials near earth. This means that the grid, cathode, and filament must be operated at a considerable negative voltage, usually in the vicinity of 2000 V. The current represented by the electron beam, however, is quite small, of the order of 100 μA. This EHT supply can be derived directly from a transformer and rectifier at supply-line frequency, but it is both safer and better to generate a high-frequency AC by means of a valve oscillator, and transform this up, rectify it and filter it. The filter condensers for this purpose can be quite small in capacitance and in physical dimensions, and cannot deliver a lethal shock. (It can, however, be most unpleasant.)

Typical circuit arrangements can be seen in Fig. 12.9. These include the

EHT supply, CRT bleed network, deflection plate connections and CRT filament supply from a special well-insulated transformer winding. Notice that the EHT rectification is done by a small valve diode (6X2) of high peak-inverse-voltage rating, whose filament is heated by high-frequency AC from a special winding on the high-frequency transformer. The oscillator runs at about 1 mc/s, and is totally enclosed in a small metal case for safety, and to avoid interference with neighbouring broadcast receivers.

To understand its operation, consider first the parallel coil and condenser between the 300 V supply and the plate of the 6BQ5 valve. Such a combination constitutes a *parallel resonant circuit*, or *tank circuit* for short. The elements of this circuit are shown in Fig. 12.2.

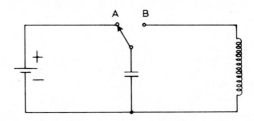

Fig. 12.2. Parallel resonant circuit.

With the switch in position *A*, the condenser charges to the voltage of the battery. If now it is switched to *B*, it discharges through the coil. In doing so, it builds up a current in the coil, with an accompanying magnetic field. When the condenser is completely discharged, this field commences to collapse and in doing so maintains current in the same direction until the condenser actually charges fully in the opposite direction. It then commences to discharge backwards and the same sequence of events is repeated in the reverse direction. In fact a sinusoidal voltage appears across the tank circuit and a sinusoidal current flows; the peak current is reached when the voltage is zero, and vice versa. During the process the original energy stored in the condenser has been transferred to the coil, then returned to the condenser, and so on, and this would continue indefinitely in a perfect condenser and inductor. The frequency at which the *oscillation* occurs is given by

$$f = \frac{1}{2\pi\sqrt{(LC)}}. \tag{12.1}$$

In a real tank circuit the inductor possesses considerable resistance, and each time current flows a little of the stored energy is lost as heat; thus the oscillation diminishes in amplitude progressively and eventually dies out, at a rate governed by the amount of resistance present.

Oscillation can also be started by establishing a current through the inductor instead of a voltage across the condenser, as in the circuit of Fig. 12.3.

If the button is pressed, current from the battery flows through the inductor. On releasing the button, oscillation will start as before, but at the point where the magnetic field has been established and is commencing to collapse.

FIG. 12.3. Establishment of oscillation in a tank circuit.

Further, in a practical circuit containing resistance in the coil, oscillation can be maintained by rhythmic pressing of the button in time with the oscillation.

Now suppose that this last circuit has, wound beside its coil, a second coil connected as shown in Fig. 12.4.

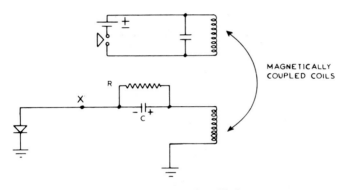

FIG. 12.4. Rectification of oscillation.

On starting the oscillation, an alternating EMF will be induced in the second coil, and this will be rectified by the diode to charge the condenser C to the peak value of the induced EMF, with the polarity shown. If the oscillation diminishes in amplitude, the resistor R will allow the condenser to discharge slowly, so that it always maintains the peak value of the alternating voltage.

If the EMF of the point X with respect to the earth point is plotted, it will be at any instant the sum of the induced EMF in the coil and the rectified condenser voltage: if the peak induced EMF is 100 V, the condenser voltage will also be 100 V, and the point X will vary with time as shown in Fig. 12.5. Now let us replace the diode with the grid and cathode of the 6BQ5, as in Fig. 12.6. These elements will behave exactly as a diode, and point X is now the grid of the valve.

On setting up an oscillation with the push button, the grid of the valve will be driven up and down with respect to the cathode just as point X was. Now the valve in this condition behaves simply as a switch. Whenever the grid is *more* than 20 V negative to earth, no current can flow through the meter.

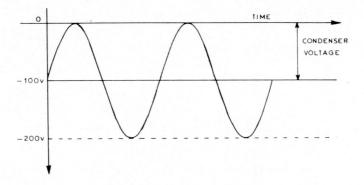

FIG. 12.5. Waveform at point X.

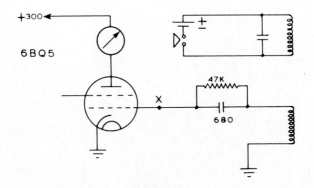

FIG. 12.6. Control of plate current.

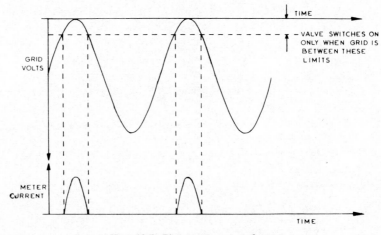

FIG. 12.7. Plate current waveform.

Whenever it is *less* than 20 V negative, it draws considerable current. So the
current flowing through the meter can be deduced graphically as is done in
Fig. 12.7.

Now it happens, by a fortunate coincidence, that these pulses of current
occur exactly at the times that the button needs to be pressed to maintain
oscillation; so instead of the battery and push button, the tank circuit can
be placed directly in place of the meter, as shown in Fig. 12.8, and oscillation

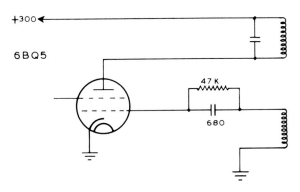

FIG. 12.8. Self-sustaining oscillation.

will be maintained indefinitely as the pulses of current pass through the coil.
The AC in the plate tank, which will have a peak value of about 250 V, is
then transformed up in the EHT winding to about 2500 V peak, and rectified
and filtered.

The CRT network is straightforward, once it is realised that all voltages
on a tube are measured with respect to the cathode. It will be seen that the
grid is returned to a variable point somewhat negative to the cathode, and
the first anode to a variable point a few hundred volts positive to the cathode.
The final anode, which is earthed, is nearly 2000 V positive to the cathode,
and so are the deflection plates.

12.4. SHIELDING

The CRT is usually surrounded by a thin magnetic shield, since the electron
beam can also be deflected magnetically, and is quite sensitive to stray
alternating fields from nearby transformers. This shield is usually made of an
alloy called mumetal, which gains its properties by being heat treated in a
reducing atmosphere after fabrication. Cutting or even sharply knocking the
shield will greatly reduce its effectiveness.

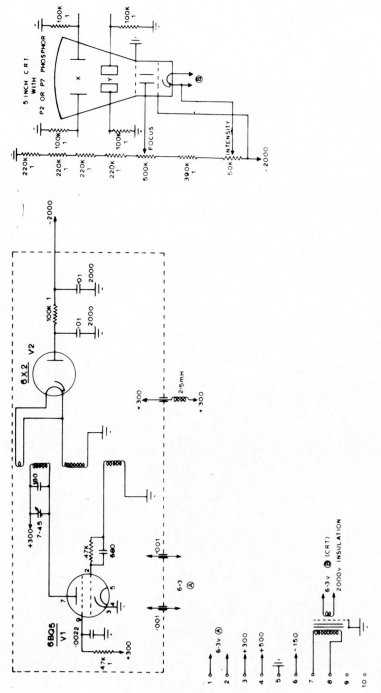

Fɪɢ. 12.9. CRT circuits and EHT supply.

12.5. SENSITIVITY

Quite large voltages have to be applied to the deflection plates to traverse
the spot across the CRT screen. Typical sensitivities are of the order of
3 V/mm. Since all tubes are designed to give a deflection accurately proportional to applied voltage, the deflection in one direction (X or Y) can be used
to compare one DC voltage with another, or to compare the peak value of an
AC voltage with a calibrating DC voltage.

Further Reading

PARR and DAVIE, *The Cathode Ray Tube*, Chapman & Hall, London, 1959.
TERMAN, *Electronic and Radio Engineering* (4th ed.), ch. 7, McGraw-Hill, New York, 1955.
TERMAN and PETTIT, *Electronic Measurements*, ch. 6, McGraw-Hill, New York, 1952.
ELMORE and SANDS, *Electronics*, ch. 5, McGraw-Hill, New York, 1959.
MIT Radiation Laboratory Series, vol. 21, ch. 17 and 18, and vol. 22, McGraw-Hill, New
York, 1948.

PRACTICAL

1. Wire your oscilloscope chassis according to the circuit of Figs. 12.9, 12.10 and 12.11,
as carefully and neatly as you can. Test by the application of batteries to the X and Y plates;
determine the deflection sensitivities. Try the effect of a permanent magnet on the beam,
with and without shielding.

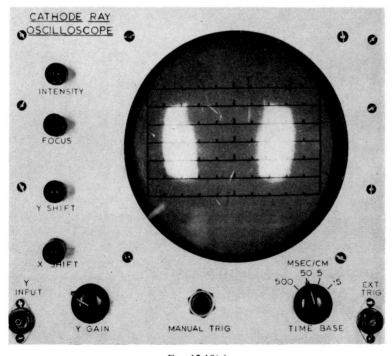

FIG. 12.10(a)

2. If an oscilloscope and a simple battery-operated LC oscillator are available, examine the plate current and voltage waveforms, and compare them with those of Fig. 12.7.

3. If an oscilloscope with slow sweep and long persistent screen is available, the circuit of Fig. 12.3 may be set up, using a very large capacitance, and a large inductor with low DC resistance. Oscillations can then be maintained by pressing the key at the right point in each cycle. (An electrolytic condenser of 5000 or 10,000 μF, an inductor of about 5 henries with a resistance of 50 ohm or less, and a 3 V battery form a suitable combination.)

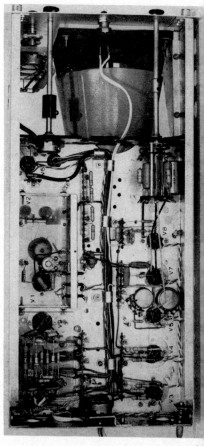

(b)   (c)

FIG. 12.10. Cathode ray oscilloscope. (a) Front. (b) Upper. (c) Lower.

FIG. 12.11. EHT supply.

CHAPTER 13

BALANCED OUTPUT AMPLIFIER

13.1. REQUIREMENTS FOR AN OUTPUT AMPLIFIER

As was discussed in Chapter 12, a pair of deflection plates in a CRT requires a considerable applied voltage to deflect the beam from one side of the CRT to the other. At 3 V/mm, a 5 in. tube will evidently require a minimum of 300 V to utilise the whole screen. It is possible to obtain this deflection with a suitable single triode or pentode amplifier, but this scheme has a number of disadvantages, and it is more usual to employ a *balanced* (or "long tailed pair") *amplifier*. This can be either a transistor or a valve amplifier. In the case of transistor amplifiers it is difficult to obtain more than 150 V to deflect the spot, and special high sensitivity CRTs are employed.

13.2. THE BALANCED AMPLIFIER

The circuit of a valve balanced amplifier is shown in Fig. 13.1; the basic transistor amplifier is identical in form, with suitable modifications in values. With the shift control set to apply zero volts to the lower valve, and nothing connected to the input terminal, the circuit is completely symmetrical. To see how it will behave, let us assume that each of the two plates is at $+200$ V, the condition of mid-point bias discussed in §9.5. By Ohm's law, this implies that a plate current of 2 mA is flowing through each valve. These two currents must unite at the common cathode connection and flow to the -150 V supply through the 40 K "long tail". Again by Ohm's law, this will produce a voltage drop across the long tail of 160 V, so the common cathode connection must be at $+10$ V with respect to earth; as in §9.5, this means that each valve has a bias of -10 V on it. Since the grid base of the 12AU7 is about 20 V, this calculated bias corresponds well with the original assumption of mid-point bias.

Since each plate is at the same voltage ($+200$) the CRT spot will be central. If now a positive voltage is applied to the input of the amplifier, the upper valve passes more plate current, and its plate and the upper CRT deflection plate will move negatively. The increasing plate current passes through the long tail, and so tends to increase the voltage drop across it, and move the common cathode connection positively. Since the grid of the lower valve is held constant by the shift control, this is in effect applying a more negative bias to the lower valve. Its plate current falls nearly as much as the plate current of the upper valve rose, and in doing so causes its plate voltage to rise, and take the lower CRT deflection plate with it. Thus the deflection plates are driven almost symmetrically about 200 V, one falling and the other

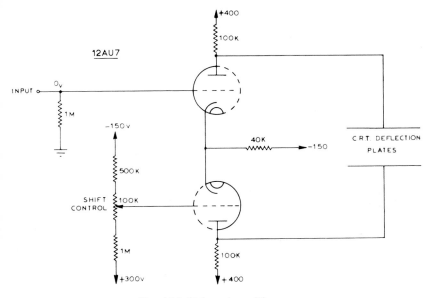

FIG. 13.1. Balanced amplifier.

rising. A negative voltage applied to the input will have the reverse effect. If the shift control is adjusted these effects occur in reverse, since the lower grid is now being driven, and the upper valve is responding to the change in current in the long tail.

13.3. ASTIGMATISM

Unless both the average voltage of the X plates and the average voltage of the Y plates are equal to the voltage of the final anode, a weak cylindrical electrostatic "lens" will be formed between them, and it will become impossible to focus the spot in both X and Y directions simultaneously. This aberration, known as *astigmatism* in optics, is normally avoided by using identical X and Y balanced amplifiers, and by operating the final anode at their mean potential. In the case discussed above, this is $+200$ V. It is usual to make this potential variable about the nominal value, to permit correction for slight inaccuracies in CRT construction. It will be seen how this has been done in Fig. 13.2.

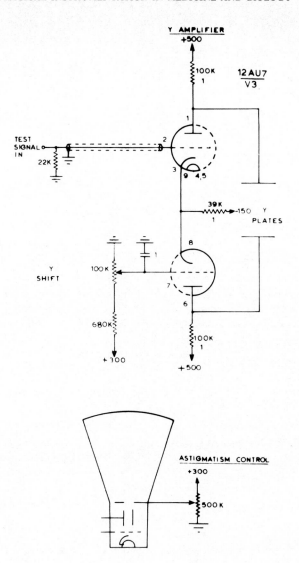

FIG. 13.2. Oscilloscope vertical amplifier.

Further Reading

(a) Valve circuits

DICKINSON, *Electrophysiological Technique*, Electronic Engineering, London, 1950.

DONALDSON, *Electronic Apparatus for Biological Research*, Butterworth, London, 1958.

PARR and DAVIE, *The Cathode Ray Tube*, Chapman & Hall, London, 1959.

(b) Transistor circuits

GILBERT, Oscilloscope timebase generator, *Mullard Technical Communications*, **7**, 276, 1964 (Mullard Ltd., London).

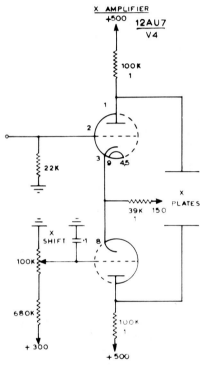

FIG. 13.3. Oscilloscope horizontal amplifier.

PRACTICAL

1.   Install the horizontal (Fig. 13.3) and vertical (Fig. 13.2) amplifiers in the oscilloscope under construction, and fit the astigmatism control to the final anode. Switch on, and test that the shift controls can move the spot over the screen. Centre the spot, and by alternate adjustments of the focus and astigmatism controls obtain the best possible focus. Keep the intensity of the spot to a minimum.

2.   Measure the DC voltages at plates and cathodes of the X and Y amplifiers, with the spot central and at the edges of the screen. Measure the CRT final anode voltage, and compare it with the mean plate voltages for both X and Y plates.

3.   Test by applying signals from two oscillators to the X and Y plates respectively. The patterns obtained in this way are known as Lissajous figures, and are often used for comparing an unknown with a standard frequency.

4.   If two low-frequency oscillators and an oscilloscope with a long persistent screen are available, the formation of Lissajous figures should be studied in slow motion.

CHAPTER 14

CATHODE FOLLOWER, EMITTER FOLLOWER

14.1. GENERAL DESCRIPTION

These circuits are used as "buffer" stages when it is desired to connect a relatively low resistance load to a relatively high resistance source of signal. Each delivers at its output a varying voltage which is an accurate replica of the applied input voltage, but which is rather smaller in amplitude; the *power* delivered is much greater than the driving power required.

14.2. THE CATHODE FOLLOWER

A typical cathode follower circuit is shown in Fig. 14.1.

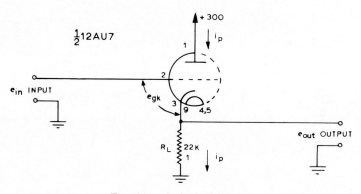

FIG. 14.1. Cathode follower.

As in an ordinary valve amplifier no current is drawn at the input under normal operating conditions.

The load resistor R_L, while still in series with the valve, is now placed between cathode and earth rather than between the $+300$ supply voltage and plate. The effect of this is that the input voltage of the amplifier is now the sum of the grid-to-cathode voltage e_{gk} and the voltage drop across the load resistor; this latter is in fact the output voltage.

$$e_{in} = e_{gk} + e_{out}$$
$$= e_{gk} + i_P R_L \quad \text{(by Ohm's law).} \quad (14.1)$$

Just as in Chapter 9, we can obtain the relationship between e_{gk} and i_p by means of a load line for the particular R_L and supply voltage used, drawn on the output characteristic for the particular valve type used. This is shown in Fig. 14.2.

Now we are in a position to deduce the graph of output voltage versus input voltage. To obtain a point on this graph, assume a value of e_{gk}: let us take for example -5 V. Then the corresponding plate current is 6·5 mA, from the load line of Fig. 14.2. Since this is flowing through the 22 K resistor, the output voltage must be, by Ohm's law, 143 V. The input voltage is then the algebraic sum of this output voltage and e_{gk}, so it must be 138 V. Proceeding in the same fashion, Table 14.1 can be built up, giving the graph of Fig. 14.3.

TABLE 14.1.

CATHODE-FOLLOWER CHARACTERISTIC

Assumed value of e_{gk}	i_p from load line	Output Voltage ($e_{out} = i_p R_L$)	Input voltage ($e_{in} = e_{gk} + e_{out}$)
0 V	9·8 mA	216 V	216 V
$-2\cdot5$	8·1	178	176
-5	6·5	143	138
$-7\cdot5$	5·2	114	107
-10	4·1	90	80
$-12\cdot5$	3·2	70	58
-15	2·4	53	38
$-17\cdot5$	1·5	33	15
-20	1·0	22	2
$-22\cdot5$	0·6	12	-10

Except for the curvature at the bottom, this graph is very close to a straight line. Its slope is the ratio of output to input volts, which is the amplification of the amplifier, and this can be seen to be rather less than unity. In fact, the gain A can be shown to be given by

$$A = \frac{\mu}{\mu + 1}, \qquad (14.2)$$

where μ is the amplification factor. For a 12AU7 with a published μ of 19, the gain will thus be 0·95. It is clear that the output voltage *follows* the input voltage.

14.3. BIAS ARRANGEMENTS

It will be seen that in the absence of an input, the output voltage is 20, and the valve is drawing little current. Without additional bias, this arrangement is suitable for positive inputs only, or for alternating signals limited to a few volts, and this is how it will be used in the oscilloscope under construction.

8

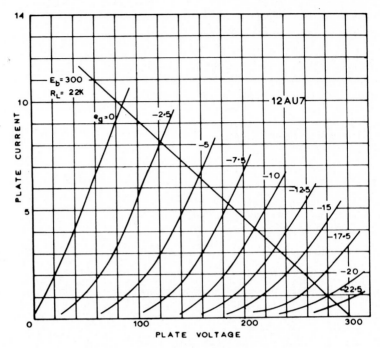

FIG. 14.2. Load line corresponding to Fig. 14.1.

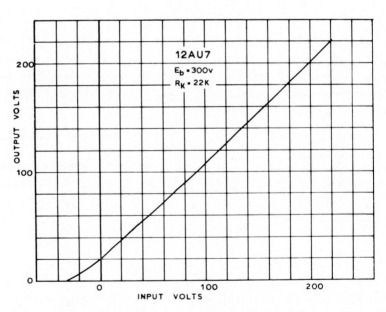

FIG. 14.3. Output voltage versus input voltage for cathode follower of Fig. 14.1.

If a sinusoidal input of say 100 peak volts were applied, the output signal would consist of little more than the positive half-waves, and this fact is sometimes used to obtain rectification of a sinusoidal wave. For true reproduction of a sinusoid or other signal which may either move positively or negatively, the cathode follower may be directly coupled to the plate of a previous amplifier as in Fig. 14.4,

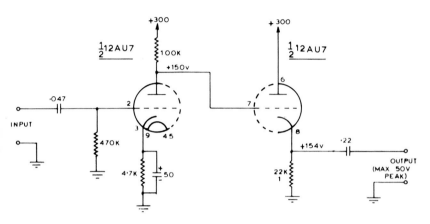

Fig. 14.4. Direct coupled cathode follower.

or it may be supplied with bias from a tapping on its own cathode resistor, as in Fig. 14.5.

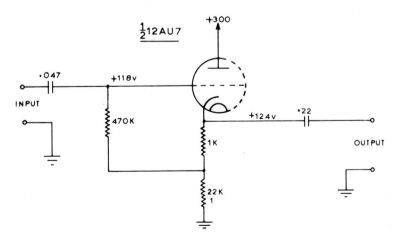

Fig. 14.5. Cathode follower with self bias.

14.4. THE EMITTER FOLLOWER

A typical emitter follower circuit is shown in Fig. 14.6. This circuit, which is also known as the common collector amplifier, resembles the cathode follower in appearance and properties.

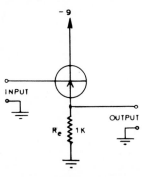

FIG. 14.6. Emitter follower.

Like the cathode follower, it is used most commonly as an impedance changing device, since its input resistance is relatively high and its output resistance relatively low. Like the conventional transistor amplifier, and unlike the cathode follower, it does require a small input *current* to drive it. Its input resistance is approximately βR_e, so in the case shown it would be about 50 K.

Since the input resistance is still fairly low, a further increase may be achieved by *cascading* two or more emitter followers, as in Fig. 14.7; each one supplies the base current of the next. This arrangement is also known as the Darlington circuit.

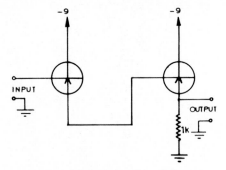

FIG. 14.7. Cascaded emitter followers.

The limit to which this process can be carried is set by the leakage current at the base of the first transistor used. It is difficult to achieve an input resistance of more than a megohm for the whole chain, even using silicon transistors, which have a very small leakage current. The available peak to peak output voltage is rather less than the supply voltage.

Further Reading

CATHODE RAY, *Wireless World*, **51**, 322 (1945).
MIT Radiation Laboratory Series, vol. 18, McGraw-Hill, New York, 1948.
Selected Semiconductor Circuits, MIL-HDBK-215, US Government Printing Office, 1960.
PETTIT, *Electronic Switching, Timing, and Pulse Circuits*, McGraw-Hill, New York, 1959.

PRACTICAL

1.   Set up a 12AU7 triode as a cathode follower as in Fig. 14.8, and provide an input voltage from a potentiometer, as shown. Plot its output versus input characteristic.

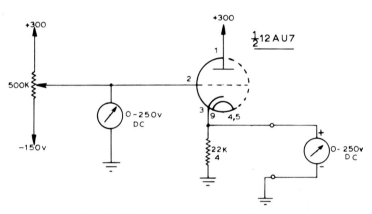

FIG. 14.8. Experimental cathode follower.

What is its measured gain? With an output voltage of 100, connect a 10 K load across the output. How does the output change? From this figure, and using Ohm's law, deduce the apparent output resistance of the cathode follower. (The theoretical value can be shown to be approximately $1/g_m$.)

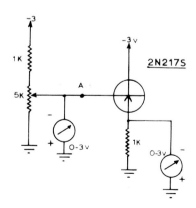

FIG. 14.9. Experimental emitter follower.

2. Set up the circuit of Fig. 14.9, and plot output voltage as a function of input voltage. (An adequate heat sink, as described in the practical work of Chapter 8, will be required.) Deduce the gain.

Insert a microammeter in series with the base lead at point *A*, and plot a graph of input current as a function of input voltage. From this graph deduce the input resistance.

3. Install cathode followers in the oscilloscope *X* and *Y* amplifier inputs as shown in the circuit of Fig. 14.10, and test the complete circuit.

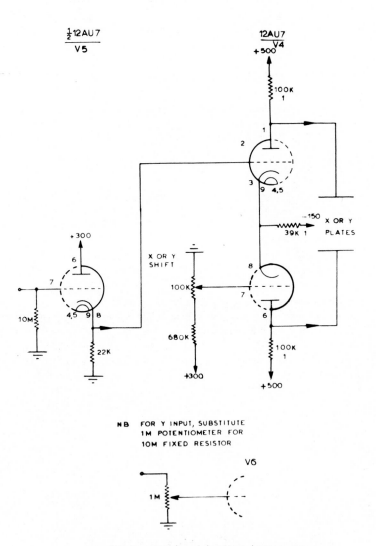

FIG. 14.10. Cathode follower input to *X* and *Y* amplifiers.

CHAPTER 15

TIME BASE GENERATION

15.1. THE FUNCTION OF A TIME BASE

The most common use of an oscilloscope is for the display of waveforms on a linear time scale. By convention, the horizontal, or X direction, is reserved for the time scale, the vertical, or Y direction, being used to represent the magnitude of the phenomenon being displayed. If the spot is deflected across the screen at a constant velocity, a linear time scale will result.

The horizontal deflection of the spot is achieved by producing a potential difference between the X deflection plates of the CRT. If the voltage applied across the X plates increases at a constant rate, the spot is deflected across the screen at a constant velocity.

In order to return the spot to the left-hand side after it has traversed the screen, the voltage across the X plates must be returned to the starting value before the next sweep can commence. The return of voltage should be as fast as possible so that little time is lost in the return of the spot (the fly-back). The ideal waveform for a linear time base is shown in Fig. 15.1, and is known as a *sawtooth*.

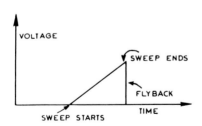

FIG. 15.1. Sawtooth waveform.

15.2. GENERATION OF A SAWTOOTH WAVEFORM

At first sight the generation of such a waveform may seem a difficult task. However, a simple approximation to a linearly rising voltage can be made by utilising the charging of a condenser through a series resistor from a voltage E_b. Such a circuit is shown in Fig. 15.2.

When the switch is closed, the voltage e across the condenser is zero. Upon opening the switch, the condenser charges towards E_b, the voltage across the condenser being given by

$$e = E_b (1 - \varepsilon^{-t/RC})$$

as was discussed in Chapter 6.

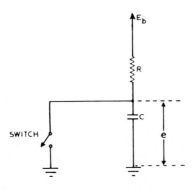

FIG. 15.2. Basic timebase.

Although e varies exponentially with time, the initial part of the curve is very nearly a straight line, as shown in Table 15.1.

TABLE 15.1.

INITIAL PORTION OF EXPONENTIAL CURVE

t	0	$0{\cdot}02RC$	$0{\cdot}04RC$	$0{\cdot}06RC$	$0{\cdot}08RC$	$0{\cdot}10RC$
e	0	$0{\cdot}020E_b$	$0{\cdot}039E_b$	$0{\cdot}058E_b$	$0{\cdot}077E_b$	$0{\cdot}095E_b$

The maximum deviation of the exponential curve from a straight line drawn from 0 to $0{\cdot}095E_b$ is about 2%, which is more than satisfactory for most purposes.

Oscilloscopes used for biological purposes often require a sweep time of 10 sec or longer, so that a time constant of 100 sec or greater will be needed. From the point of view of stability a resistor of greater than 10M or so is undesirable, so that a large polyester dielectric condenser of high quality is called for. Paper dielectric condensers are in general quite unsuitable owing to their property of "dielectric soakage"; a short while after a rapid and apparently complete discharge they will be found to be partially charged although not connected to any external circuit. It is therefore desirable to find some means of reducing the value of capacitance needed. One suitable arrangement is the "bootstrap" circuit, so called because it raises itself by its own bootstraps. It is of American design.

15.3. OPERATION OF THE BOOTSTRAP CIRCUIT

Consider the circuit of Fig. 15.3 with the switch initially closed.

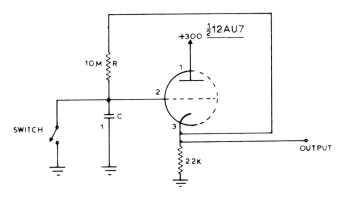

FIG. 15.3. Bootstrap circuit.

In this condition the grid of the cathode follower is earthed and C is discharged. A 12AU7 with a 22 K cathode resistor and a supply voltage of $+300$ V will, with its grid earthed, have a cathode voltage of $+20$ V. This voltage is applied to the top of the charging resistor R, in the position to which the supply voltage is usually connected for a time base. Consequently, a very small current, given by Ohm's law as 2 μA (20/10 M), will flow through R and the switch to earth.

On opening the switch, this current will flow into the condenser, and commence to charge it. Two microamperes is 2 microcoulombs per second by definition. Since the condenser has a capacitance of 1 μF and

$$e = \frac{q}{C},$$

its voltage will commence to rise by 2 V/s, starting from zero. This rising voltage is, however, applied to the grid of the cathode follower. If the cathode follower had a gain of unity, its cathode would rise at the same rate, remaining always 20 V higher; the charging current would remain constant at 2 μA and the condenser would charge linearly. In fact the gain is rather less than unity, and so the initial 20 V gradually diminishes as charging proceeds, eventually disappearing as the cathode follower reaches zero bias (at about 200 V input). Thus the charging curve will approximate to an exponential rise, of which only the first 10% is used. If the charging resistor had been returned directly to a 200 V supply, without using the bootstrap arrangement, a 10 μF condenser would have been needed for an initial rise of 2 V/s. The capacitance has thus in effect been multiplied ten times.

15.4. TRANSISTOR TIME BASES

In the example quoted in §15.3, the condenser charging current was 2 μA. It is clear that if even a small fraction of this were to be diverted through the grid of the valve, the operation of the circuit would be grossly impaired.

It is relatively easy to obtain a valve which does not load the charging circuit in this fashion, but a transistor, which is a current-operated device, will obviously constitute an appreciable load. This can be overcome to some

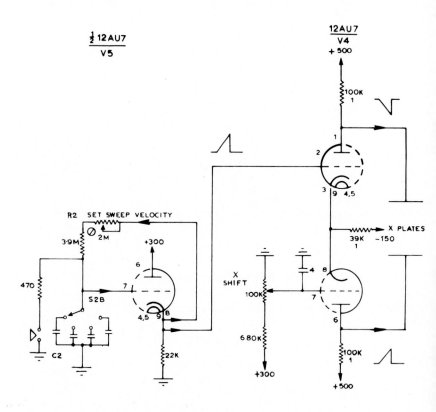

S2 SWEEP VELOCITY

POSITION	VELOCITY	C2(C2R2 SETS SWEEP VELOCITY)	
1	0.5 MSEC/CM	680	
2	5	.0068	RATIOS ACCURATE TO 1%
3	50	.068	
4	500	.68	

FIG. 15.4. Bootstrap time base.

extent by the use of larger currents and correspondingly larger condensers, but for very slow time bases it is simpler to use a valve. At faster speeds transistors are quite suitable, and a typical circuit is given by Gilbert (see the reference at the end of this chapter).

Further Reading

MIT Radiation Laboratory Series, vol. 19, p. 267, McGraw-Hill, New York, 1949.
STRAUSS, *Wave Generation and Shaping*, McGraw-Hill, New York, 1961.
GILBERT, Oscilloscope timebase generator, *Mullard Technical Communications*, 7, 276, 1964 (Mullard Ltd., London).

PRACTICAL

1. Connect up the bootstrap circuit shown in Fig. 15.3, but connect the top of the 10 M resistor to +300 V instead of to the cathode of the valve. Use a polyester condenser for C. Using a multimeter to measure the output voltage of the cathode follower and a stopwatch, plot the charging curve as a function of time. Measure the initial rate of rise in volts per second.

2. Connect the top of the 10M resistor to the cathode of the valve, and plot the charging curve that results. Measure the initial rate of rise, in volts per second, and compare with the result obtained in question 1.

3. Install a bootstrap time base in the oscilloscope under construction, following the circuit of Fig. 15.4. Test its operation on all ranges, and set the internal calibration resistor by means of a calibrated oscillator.

N.B. When this oscilloscope is being constructed by groups of students, it is suggested that the timing condensers in the bootstrap circuit, and also those used on the same switch assembly in Chapter 17, be selected and mounted on the switch assembly prior to the practical session.

CHAPTER 16

ASTABLE MULTIVIBRATOR

16.1. THE TRANSISTOR AS A SWITCH

In Chapter 8 it was shown how a transistor could be used as an amplifier, with a base bias current such that the collector voltage lay about half-way between zero and the supply voltage. An equally common use for the transistor is as a switch: the circuit is arranged so that the collector current is either completely cut off, or completely turned on, and transition from one state to the other is made as rapidly as possible.

For the collector current to be completely turned off, it is sufficient to make the base current zero. Under these conditions there is no voltage drop across the collector load, and the collector voltage is equal to the supply voltage. If the base is *reverse biased* (by applying a positive voltage to the base of a *PNP* transistor, or a negative voltage to the base of an *NPN*) the same conditions will hold, but only a limited voltage can be applied in this fashion without causing the base-to-emitter diode to break down. The permissible peak inverse voltage is usually listed in transistor data books as V_{EB}. The situation in a cut off *PNP* transistor is shown in Fig. 16.1a.

For the collector current to be completely turned on, a sufficient base current must be supplied. A fully on transistor may have a collector voltage as low as 0·2 V or less, so practically the whole supply voltage appears across the collector load (Fig. 16.1b).

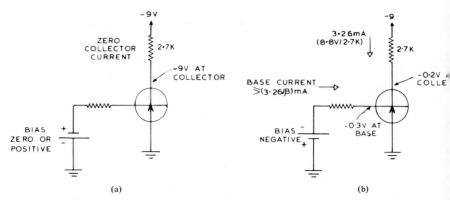

(a)   (b)

FIG. 16.1. *PNP* transistor as a switch. (a) Cut off. (b) Fully conducting.

The collector current can readily be calculated by Ohm's law; in the figure it will be 3·26 mA. Remembering that the collector current is approximately β times the base current, it will be seen that a base current of at least 3·26/β must be supplied to raise the collector current to this value. A base current greater than this will produce no further effect: the transistor is said to be *saturated*. When the base current is subsequently cut off, there will be a slight delay before the collector current cuts off. This is the storage time; it may be as high as 5 μsec in general purpose transistors, and constitute a serious limitation in high-speed switching circuits. It is much less in modern transistors designed for use as switches.

16.2. THE VALVE AS A SWITCH

Valves may also be used as switches, and have been so used ever since their inception. (An example has already been encountered in the EHT supply circuit in Chapter 12.) Typical operating conditions in the off and on conditions are shown in Fig. 16.2.

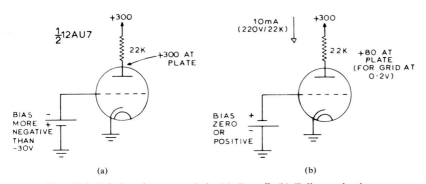

FIG. 16.2. Triode valve as a switch. (a) Cut off. (b) Fully conducting.

In the cut-off condition, as in the transistor, there is no plate current, and the plate voltage is equal to the supply voltage. In the case of the valve there is no serious limitation to the inverse bias voltage between grid and cathode; it may be as much as several hundred volts if the circuit so requires.

In the "fully conducting" condition the valve is not nearly so effective a switch as the transistor. There is no condition corresponding to saturation, but in most circuits the grid is never driven more than a fraction of a volt positive. Under these circumstances the plate voltage still represents a considerable fraction of the supply voltage.

16.3. THE MULTIVIBRATOR

This name is applied to a general class of circuits for generating rectangular pulses of voltage. A multivibrator may be (i) astable, in which case a continuous succession of pulses is produced, (ii) monostable, in which case one pulse only is produced when the action is initiated by an incoming trigger pulse, or (iii) bistable, in which case a pulse is started by one incoming trigger pulse and terminated by a second. The circuit is very similar for each application, the difference lying only in the method of coupling the two halves of the circuit. All three types may be constructed using either transistors or valves. Except for the generation of slow pulses, transistors are incomparably superior in these circuits, and their use has become general. (In the oscilloscope under construction a valve multivibrator has been retained, since a slow time base is required for the investigation of biological waveforms.)

16.4. THE TRANSISTOR ASTABLE MULTIVIBRATOR

The circuit of a typical astable multivibrator is shown in Fig. 16.3.

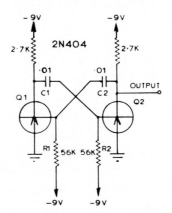

FIG. 16.3. Transistor astable multivibrator.

This circuit will alternate between a condition in which Q1 is cut off and Q2 is saturated, and a condition in which the reverse is true, at a rate set by the values of C1 and C2. To understand its operation, assume that initially Q1 is cut off and Q2 is saturated, as in Fig. 16.4.

The collector of Q2 will be at -0.2 V, and its base will be at -0.3 V, since it is saturated. Q1 is cut off, so its collector will be at -9 V, and its base at some positive voltage (its exact value will be determined later). The first three of these voltages are quite stable, but that at the base of Q1 is not. It appears at the top of R1, which has -9 V at its lower end. So by Ohm's law,

a current must be flowing through R1, and this can only be altering the
charge on C2, and thus causing the base of Q1 to move exponentially towards

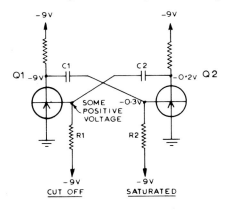

FIG. 16.4. Astable multivibrator: assumed initial state.

-9 V, with a time constant of R_1C_2. These conditions are shown by point 1
in each of the diagrams of Fig. 16.5.

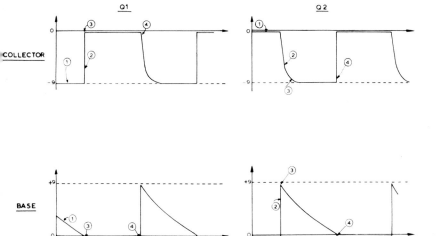

FIG. 16.5. Waveforms in astable multivibrator.

After a short time the base of Q1 will actually become negative (point 2 in
Fig. 16.5). As soon as this occurs Q1 commences to conduct. Its collector
voltage moves positively from -9 V, and since C1 cannot change its state
of charge instantly, the base of Q2 also moves positively. This reduces Q2
collector current, and hence its collector voltage moves negatively. This in
turn rapidly drives the base of Q1 further negative by way of C1, and the

process becomes cumulative. In a period of a few microseconds or less Q1 is driven to saturation, with its base-to-emitter diode forward biased. Its collector goes to -0.2 V, a change of 8.8 V positively. This sudden change moves the base of Q2 8.8 V positively also, from its original -0.3 V to $+8.5$ V, and cuts Q2 off hard (point 3 in Fig. 16.5). The two transistors have now changed roles. C1 now commences to discharge just as C2 did previously, and presently the circuit reverts to its original state by the reverse of the process described above (point 4 in Fig. 16.5). This alternation proceeds indefinitely, generating a series of rectangular pulses at the collector of each transistor. They will have an amplitude of 8.8 V, and a duration governed by the time constants R_1C_2 and R_2C_1.

16.5. THE VALVE ASTABLE MULTIVIBRATOR

The circuit of a typical valve astable multivibrator is shown in Fig. 16.6. Its operation is closely similar to that of the transistor circuit.

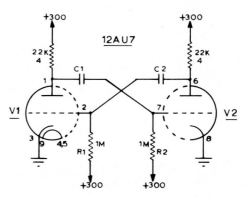

FIG. 16.6. Valve astable multivibrator.

16.6. CALCULATION OF PULSE DURATIONS

A consideration of the exponential charging curve in the case of the transistor multivibrator of Fig. 16.3 shows that the duration of the negative rectangular pulse at the collector of Q1 is given by $0.7R_1C_2$, and the duration of the similar pulse at the collector of Q2 is given by $0.7R_2C_1$. These durations do not have to be the same, but it is not possible to make them differ by a ratio of more than about 5:1 without interfering with the operation of the circuit. If it is desired to construct a multivibrator with a range of pulse durations, it is usual to have a series of fixed values of C_1 or C_2 selected by a switch, and to provide intermediate values by making R_1 or R_2 variable. It should be noted that the maximum value of R_2 or R_1 that can be used is that which just permits sufficient base current to saturate the transistor, as discussed in §16.1 above.

In the case of the valve multivibrator of Fig. 16.6, the duration of the positive rectangular pulse at the plate of V1 is given by $0·5R_1C_2$, and the duration of the similar pulse at the plate of V2 is given by $0·5R_2C_1$. As in the case of the transistor circuit, these may differ, but a 10:1 asymmetry is about the maximum possible. There is no stringent upper limit to the values of R_2 and R_1 in the valve circuit; a range between 100 K and 10 M is common.

16.7. DIFFERENTIATION OF OUTPUT PULSE

It frequently happens that a train of sharp pulses at regular intervals is required, either for timing other events, or for triggering a subsequent monostable or bistable multivibrator. In this case an astable multivibrator is used, and its output pulse is *differentiated* by means of a small condenser and resistor. (This is not accurate differentiation in the mathematical sense, but an approximation to it.) Fig. 16.7 shows how the output of the circuit of Fig. 16.3 will appear before and after differentiation in this fashion.

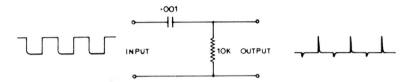

FIG. 16.7. Differentiating circuit.

The negative-going edge of each pulse produces little output, since it is too slow. The positive-going edge is reproduced as a sharp pip of height almost equal to that of the original pulse and of duration governed by the time constant of the differentiating circuit.

Further Reading

MILLMAN and TAUB, *Pulse and Digital Circuits*, McGraw-Hill, New York, 1956.
MIT Radiation Laboratory Series, vol. 19, McGraw-Hill, New York, 1949.
STRAUSS, *Wave Generation and Shaping*, McGraw-Hill, New York, 1961.
PETTIT, *Electronic Switching, Timing, and Pulse Circuits*, McGraw-Hill, New York, 1959.
Basic Theory and Application of Transistors, TM11-690, US Army, 1959.
Selected Semiconductor Circuits, MIL-HDBK-215, US Government Printing Office, 1960.
Switching Transistor Handbook, Motorola Inc., Phoenix, Arizona, 1963.
Preferred Circuits, NAVWEPS 16-1-519-2, US National Bureau of Standards 1960 and supplements.
The Transistor—Theory and Applications, Philips Electron Tube Division, Einthoven, 1963.
Mullard Reference Manual of Transistor Circuits, Wrightman, London, 1960.
GE Transistor Manual (7th ed.), General Electric, New York, 1964.
ELMORE and SANDS, *Electronics*, McGraw-Hill, New York, 1949.

PRACTICAL

1. Using the circuit of Fig. 16.3, but substituting 1 μF polyester condensers for C1 and C2, assemble an astable multivibrator on a length of resistor tag strip or a piece of matrix board. Any general purpose or switching *PNP* transistor may be used. What pulse durations do you expect? Use your partially constructed oscilloscope to examine the waveform generated at each base and each collector. Retain this assembly for use in the next two practical sessions.

2. If a commercial oscilloscope is available, examine the output of the astable multivibrator with 0·01 μF condensers used for C1 and C2.

CHAPTER 17

MONOSTABLE MULTIVIBRATOR

The circuit of a typical monostable multivibrator is shown in Fig. 17.1.

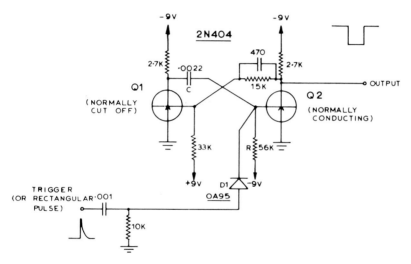

FIG. 17.1. Transistor monostable multivibrator.

This circuit remains quiescent, with Q1 cut off and Q2 saturated, until a positive pulse is fed in by way of the trigger terminal. It then immediately reverses its state, remains reversed for a time determined by RC, and finally reverts to the quiescent state. These changes cause the generation of a rectangular negative-going pulse at the collector of Q2, which may be used to turn on or off a subsequent circuit for a set time, or be differentiated to give a positive-going pulse delayed on the incoming positive pulse by a set time.

The circuit is often referred to as a "flip-flop", because the input trigger flips the circuit, which then flops back after a desired interval.

Figure 17.1 should be carefully compared with Fig. 16.3 showing the astable multivibrator. The difference will be seen to lie in the fact that one

119

cross-coupling condenser and resistor combination (R_1C_2 of Fig. 16.3) has been replaced by a direct coupling consisting of two resistors, the upper of which is paralleled by a 470 pF "speed up" condenser which compensates for stray capacitance at the base of Q1. In addition, the base resistor of Q1 is returned to a source of positive bias.

The two resistors are so proportioned that in the resting state the base of Q1 lies at about $+3$ V, and Q1 is accordingly cut off with its collector at -9 V. Q2 is saturated, since its base is returned to -9 V through 56 K. Its base will thus be at about -0.3 V, and its collector at about -0.2 V. These conditions are shown at point 1 in Fig. 17.2. All of them are stable.

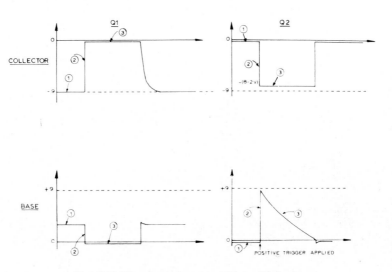

FIG. 17.2. Waveforms in monostable multivibrator.

A positive trigger pulse (point 2) applied to the input terminal will be transferred through the diode D1 to the base of Q2, and will cut Q2 off. Its collector will thus move negatively, and will carry the base of Q1 far enough negative to saturate Q1. The collector of Q1 will move positively by 8.8 V to -0.2 V, and since C cannot change its state of charge instantly, the base of Q2 will also be moved positively by 9.8 V, to 8.5 V. This will hold Q2 cut off, although the trigger pulse which initiated the whole sequence will disappear after a few microseconds.

As in the astable circuit, C now commences to discharge exponentially through R (point 3), and the base of Q2 moves negatively from 8.5 V. When it actually becomes negative, Q2 commences to draw current, a cumulative action takes place, and the circuit abruptly flops back to its resting condition.

17.2. TRIGGERING OF TRANSISTOR MONOSTABLE MULTIVIBRATOR

The purpose of diode D1 is to isolate the multivibrator circuit from the trigger input during the active cycle. As soon as the base of Q2 goes positive on receipt of the trigger input (Fig. 17.2), D1 will be reverse biased, and the waveform at the base of Q2 will not appear at the trigger input. In the quiescent state, D1 is slightly forward biased and the positive trigger pulse passes it readily. It has the additional advantage that any negative pulses which may appear at the trigger input during the active cycle cannot pass, and so there is no risk of their terminating the active cycle prematurely.

17.3. THE VALVE MONOSTABLE MULTIVIBRATOR

A typical circuit of a valve monostable multivibrator is shown in Fig. 17.3. As in the case of the astable multivibrator, its operation is similar to that of the transistor version. The considerations in the choice of R and C are identical with those discussed in §16.6.

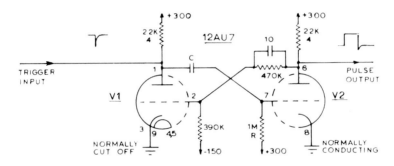

FIG. 17.3. Valve monostable multivibrator.

17.4. TRIGGERING OF VALVE MONOSTABLE MULTIVIBRATOR

In the case of valve circuits, the incoming trigger is normally injected by way of the plate opposite to the grid where the trigger is required. If Figs. 17.3 and 17.1 are compared, it will be seen that in each case the trigger will reach the right-hand grid or base to turn off a normally conducting valve or transistor.

If a large negative trigger is available, a diode may be used in the valve trigger input line just as it is in the transistor trigger line. However, if a smaller positive trigger pulse is available, a convenient method of injection which provides amplification, inversion of the pulse, isolation of the trigger input from the multivibrator, and immunity to spurious negative pulses can be used. This is shown in Fig. 17.4.

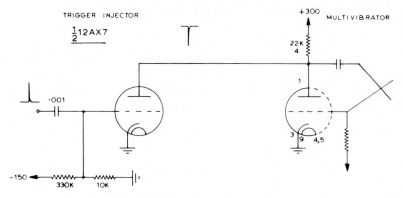

FIG. 17.4. Positive triggering of valve multivibrator.

The trigger injector valve is normally just cut off by the bias applied at its grid, but a pulse injected into it will cause it to draw a pulse of current through the 22 K resistor, and thus generate a negative-going trigger at its plate.

Further Reading

As for Chapter 16.

PRACTICAL

1. Using the circuit of Fig. 17.1, but substituting a 0·22 μF condenser for C, assemble a monostable multivibrator on a length of resistor tag strip or a piece of matrix board. What pulse duration do you expect? Trigger it from the output of the astable multivibrator constructed in Chapter 16, and examine its waveforms on your partially constructed oscilloscope. Retain this assembly for modification in the next practical session.

2. Temporarily substitute a 50 μF 12 V electrolytic condenser for C, being careful to connect the positive end to the transistor base, and trigger the circuit momentarily by connecting the trigger input to the +9 V supply, and then earthing it. Examine the waveforms with your multimeter.

3. Install the monostable multivibrator and trigger injector in your oscilloscope, as shown in Fig. 17.5. By the addition of an extra triode valve as shown, it may be used to turn the time base on and off, and thus start the time base when an incoming trigger pulse is received. If this trigger pulse is itself derived from the waveform to be examined, a stationary pattern which can be examined in detail will be obtained on the screen.

4. Use your complete oscilloscope time base to examine the waveforms of your transistor multivibrator.

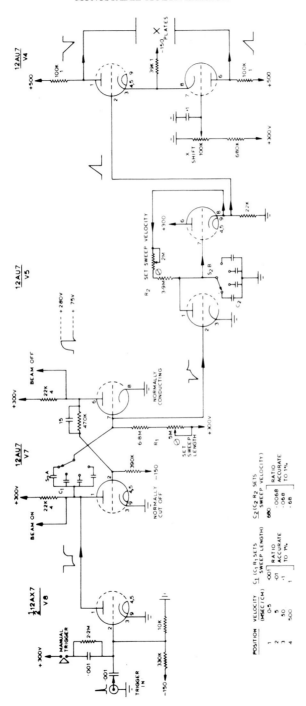

FIG. 17.5. Complete oscilloscope time base.

CHAPTER 18

BISTABLE MULTIVIBRATOR

18.1. THE TRANSISTOR BISTABLE MULTIVIBRATOR

This circuit, which is sometimes known as the Eccles–Jordan multi-vibrator, has two possible stable states. It may be transferred from one to the other or back again by the application of suitable trigger pulses. A typical circuit is shown in Fig. 18.1.

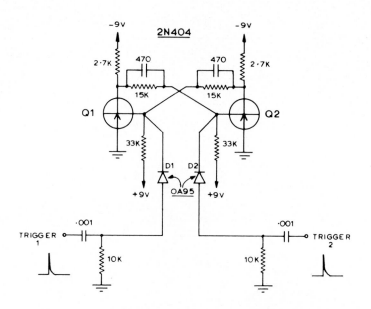

FIG. 18.1. Transistor bistable multivibrator.

This circuit should be carefully compared with those of Figs. 17.1 and 16.3. To understand its operation, assume that initially Q1 is saturated (point 1 in Fig. 18.2). Its collector will be at about -0.2 V, and this will put the base of Q2 at about $+3$ V, holding Q2 cut off, and effectively out of the circuit. This means that the base of Q1 is placed at the junction point of a voltage divider. The lower end goes to $+9$ V through 33 K, and the upper end to -9 V through 17·7 K (15 K $+$ 2·7 K). In the absence of Q1, a current of 0·36 mA

124

(18 V/50·7 K) would flow through this divider, and this would place the junction point at − 2·7 V. However, this is obviously more than sufficient to forward bias Q1; the initial assumption that Q1 was saturated is in fact true. Since Q1 is saturated, we may assume its base voltage to be about − 0·3 V. The base-to-emitter diode is forward biased, and thus is passing sufficient current to reduce the − 2·7 V to − 0·3 V. All these conditions are stable, and the circuit can remain in this state indefinitely.

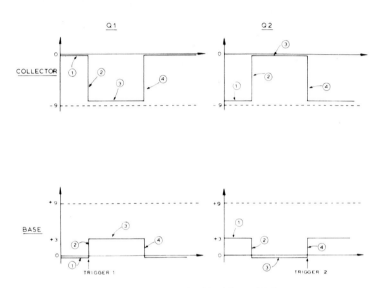

Fig. 18.2. Waveforms in bistable multivibrator.

If now a positive pulse is applied to the trigger 1 input, it will pass through diode D1 and immediately cut Q1 off (point 2). Now Q1 will be effectively out of circuit; its collector will move negatively, and by the same argument as was stated above will take the base of Q2 sufficiently negative to saturate Q2. The collector of Q2 will fall to − 0·2 V, and this will take the base of Q1 to +3 V. All these conditions are also stable (point 3), and so when the trigger disappears the circuit will remain indefinitely in the reversed state, with Q1 cut off and Q2 saturated. By the application of a positive pulse to the trigger 2 input, the circuit may be restored to its original condition (point 4). An output may be taken from either collector, as required.

18.2. SCALE-OF-TWO CIRCUIT

Trigger inputs 1 and 2 in Fig. 18.1 may be combined in the arrangement shown in Fig. 18.3.

In this case successive input pulses switch the multivibrator from one state to the other and back again. D1 and D2 act as *steering diodes* for the pulses. If, for example, Q1 is saturated and Q2 cut off, Q1 base is at -0.3 V, and Q2 base at $+3$ V, and D1 is conducting and D2 cut off. An incoming positive

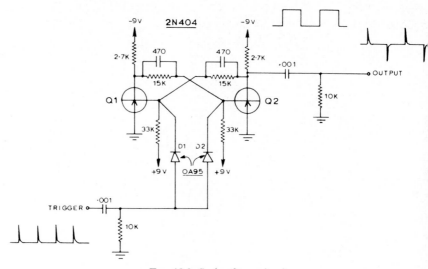

FIG. 18.3. Scale-of-two circuit.

pulse will accordingly be steered to Q1 rather than to Q2, and will reverse the condition of the circuit. This will reverse the bias on the bases of Q1 and Q2, and hence on D1 and D2; D1 will be cut off and D2 conducting. Thus the next pulse will be steered to Q2, and so on. If the output from a collector is taken, it will be a series of rectangular waves, one for every two incoming pulses. Differentiating this, as in Fig. 18.3, will yield a train of alternate positive and negative pulses, with one *positive* pulse for each two incoming positive pulses.

This circuit is known as a binary or scale-of-two counter, and is basic both in high-speed counters for radioisotope measurements, and in digital computers. Applications will be discussed in Chapters 24 and 27.

18.3. OSCILLOSCOPE BEAM SWITCHING

It is desirable in an oscilloscope that only the forward part of the sweep is visible, the electron beam being cut off during the flyback and while the spot is stationary. This is especially important in CRTs with a type P7 phosphor, which can be very easily burned.

This beam switching can be achieved by applying a considerable negative bias to the CRT when the spot is not wanted, and reducing it to a value giving the desired intensity when it is. One of the most reliable methods of performing this operation is to use a bistable multivibrator floating at the full EHT potential and acting as a switch. It may be triggered on or off through small high-insulation condensers, as required. As one plate rises or falls it moves the CRT grid from cut-off to a suitable operating bias, and vice versa. Either transistors or valves can be used for this purpose.

18.4. THE VALVE BISTABLE MULTIVIBRATOR

The circuit of a typical valve bistable multivibrator is shown in Fig. 18.4.

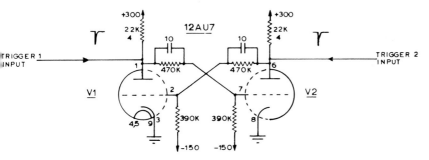

FIG. 18.4. Valve bistable multivibrator.

As in the case of the astable and monostable circuits, its operation and waveforms are very similar to those of the transistor bistable multivibrator.

Further Reading

As for Chapter 16.

PRACTICAL

1. Using the circuit of Fig. 18.1, but omitting the trigger inputs and diodes, assemble a bistable multivibrator on a length of resistor tag strip or matrix board. It may be triggered for experimental purposes by momentarily connecting the base of the conducting transistor to +9 V. Measure the voltage at each base and collector for each stable state, taking care that application of your meter has not accidentally triggered the circuit. (Leave one meter attached to a collector and measure with a second.)

2. Connect the bistable multivibrator as a scale-of-two circuit as shown in Fig. 18.3, and drive it with the astable multivibrator constructed in Chapter 16. Examine the waveforms produced, using your partially constructed oscilloscope.

3. Install the beam control switch in the oscilloscope under construction, as shown in Fig. 18.5. This circuit derives its power from the EHT supply, as will be seen by an examination of the drawing. Its plate resistor values are rather higher than usual, to minimise the supply current required, and a 12AX7 valve is used for the same reason. The details of this assembly may be seen in Fig. 18.6.

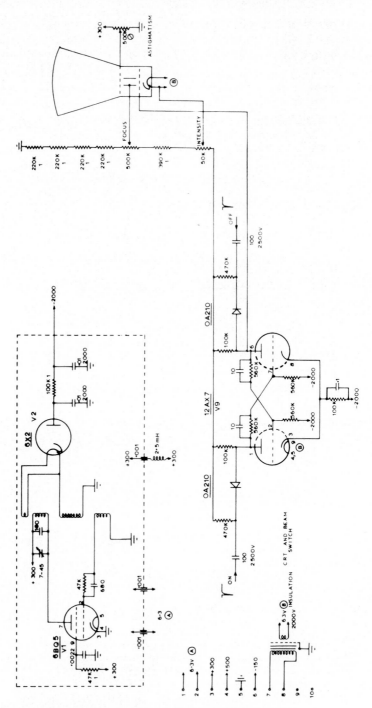

FIG. 18.5. Oscilloscope beam control multivibrator.

FIG. 18.6. Beam control multivibrator assembly.

CHAPTER 19

HIGH-FREQUENCY RESPONSE

19.1. LOW-PASS FILTER

A low-pass filter is one which allows low frequencies to pass, but attenuates high frequencies. The simplest and most important type is the RC network shown in Fig. 19.1.

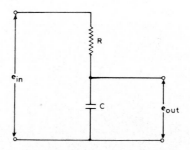

FIG. 19.1. Simple low-pass filter.

The impedance of the condenser to an alternating voltage of frequency f is

$$Z_c = \frac{1}{2\pi fC} \quad \text{(refer to Chapter 6)}$$

and the impedance of the resistance is simply R at all frequencies. These are added at right angles to give the total impedance Z_{total}, as shown in Fig. 19.2.

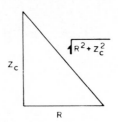

FIG. 19.2. Impedance triangle for low-pass filter.

$$Z_{\text{total}} = \sqrt{(R^2 + Z_C^2)}. \tag{19.1}$$

Now, since the network is merely a voltage divider,

$$e_{out} = \frac{Z_C}{Z_{total}} \cdot e_{in}. \tag{19.2}$$

If we define the *gain G* of the network as

$$G = \frac{e_{out}}{e_{in}}, \tag{19.3}$$

then

$$G = \frac{Z_C}{Z_{total}}$$

$$= \frac{Z_C}{\sqrt{(R^2 + Z_C^2)}}$$

$$= \frac{1}{\sqrt{(R^2 + Z_C^2)/Z_C^2}}$$

$$= \frac{1}{\sqrt{[(R^2/Z_C^2) + 1]}}. \tag{19.4}$$

Now since $Z_C = 1/2\pi fC$, at low frequencies it is very large, and falls inversely with f. At some frequency, which we will call f_0, it will become equal to R. Then at f_0

$$G = \frac{1}{\sqrt{(1 + 1)}}$$

$$= \frac{1}{\sqrt{2}} = 0.707 \tag{19.5}$$

This frequency is an easy one to calculate, and is referred to as the *cut-off frequency* of the filter. Since at f_0

$$R = \frac{1}{2\pi f_0 C},$$

then

$$f_0 = \frac{1}{2\pi RC}. \tag{19.6}$$

Gains are frequently expressed as the logarithm of a ratio rather than the ratio itself; this permits addition rather than multiplication to obtain the overall gain of a chain of amplifiers or filters. The gain in *decibels A* is defined as

$$A = 20 \log\ G$$

$$\text{For } G = \frac{1}{\sqrt{2}}, \quad A = 20 \log \frac{1}{\sqrt{2}}$$

$$= -10 \log 2$$

$$= -3 \text{ db.} \tag{19.7}$$

f_0 is thus also referred to as the *3 db point* of the filter.

If the gain is calculated for a number of frequencies which are fractions or multiples of f_0, a general curve can be plotted for the filter as in Fig. 19.3.

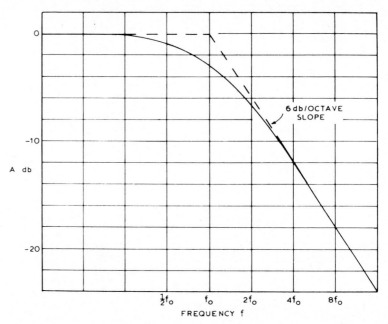

FIG. 19.3. General curve for low pass filter.

For convenience, f is also plotted on a logarithmic scale, and it will be seen that the curve soon falls at a constant rate, by 6 db for every twofold increase in frequency—every *octave*, in musical terminology. This is characteristic of this type of filter.

Low-pass filters are frequently used in biological amplifiers to remove interfering signals of higher frequency than the one being observed; for example, to remove interference from muscular activity from an ECG. For reasonable attenuation by a single filter, the unwanted signal must have a frequency at least ten times the desired one (giving $A = -20$ db, or $G = 0.1$, as in Fig. 19.3). However, two or more filters may be inserted at different points in an amplifier; two filters will give a fall of 12 db per octave, three 18 db per octave, and so on. Filters can be directly connected to one another with little loss in effectiveness if each has the same RC value, but R is increased progressively. Consider the filter of Fig. 19.4.

For each section separately,

$$f_0 = \frac{1}{2\pi \times 0.0016} \text{ c/s}$$
$$= 100 \text{ c/s}.$$

Each section alone will attenuate at 6 db per octave at frequencies well above f_0, and the three together at nearly 18 db per octave.

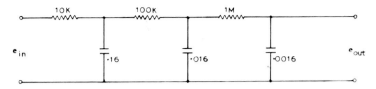

Fig. 19.4. Tapered low-pass filter.

Apart from their deliberate use, low-pass filters inevitably occur in amplifiers as a result of stray capacitances. For example, stray capacitances to earth exist at the plate of every valve, partly within the valve itself, partly due to the input capacitance of the following valve, and partly due to the wiring. A typical figure for a pentode amplifier, as shown in Fig. 19.5, would be 10 pF.

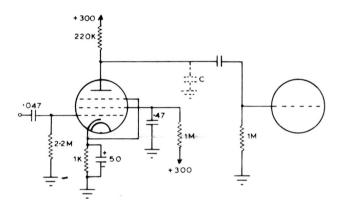

Fig. 19.5. Pentode amplifier, showing stray capacitance C.

The value R associated with this stray capacitance C is the load resistor of the valve, in parallel with both the internal resistance of the valve (about 2 M) and the grid leak of the following valve.

If C is 10 pF and R is 150 K,

$$f_0 = \frac{1}{2\pi \times 0\cdot15 \times 10^{-5}} \text{ c/s}$$

$$= \frac{10^6}{3\pi} \text{ c/s}$$

$$= 106 \text{ kc/s}.$$

At frequencies above this the amplification will fall off seriously.

10

A similar situation exists in mechanical recording systems, such as ink writing recorders, in which the mechanical constants form a low-pass filter to limit the high-frequency response.

It should be noted that f_0 *alone does not necessarily specify* the ability of an amplifier or recorder to reproduce faithfully a complex waveform; low-pass filters also change the *phase* of the higher-frequency components, and this may produce intolerable distortion. A better way of looking at a low-pass filter is in terms of its response to a sudden change in applied voltage—its *transient* response. If an abrupt 1 V step is applied to the input of the simple filter of Fig. 19.6, the condenser will charge exponentially with a time constant given by RC, towards 1 V.

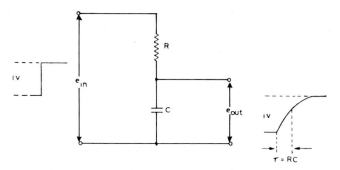

FIG. 19.6. Transient response of low-pass filter.

The *rise time* of the filter is defined arbitrarily as the time taken for the output to rise from 10 to 90% of its final value; in this case it will take 2·2 time constants.

The initial portion of the rise is approximately linear; over this region the output closely approaches the integral of the input, and the filter is sometimes loosely described as an integrating network.

The relationships between f_0, the rise time and the time constant are summarised in Fig. 19.7.

FIG. 19.7. Relations between cut off frequency, rise time, and time constant of a simple low-pass filter.

More complex low-pass filters will not give a simple exponential rise in output when a step voltage is applied, and the foregoing rules do not apply; however, the rise time is still defined as above.

Any amplifier and any mechanical recording system will have a character-istic rise time, which will limit its ability to respond to fast changes in input. Provided, however, that the rise time is short in terms of the phenomena being examined, no significant degradation of the waveforms being observed will result. Table 20.1 at the end of Chapter 20 summarises the rise time requirements for accurate reproduction of various types of biological signals.

Further Reading

SCROGGIE, *Second Thoughts on Radio Theory*, p. 212, Iliffe, London, 1955.
DONALDSON, *Electronic Apparatus for Biological Research*, Butterworth, London, 1958.
PETTIT, *Electronic Switching, Timing, and Pulse Circuits*, McGraw-Hill, New York, 1959.
VALLEY and WALLMAN, MIT Radiation Laboratory Series, vol. 18, McGraw-Hill, New York, 1948.

PRACTICAL

1. Set up a simple RC low-pass filter, using $R = 33$ K, $C = 0.01$. At what frequency is Z_c equal to R? Drive it from an audio-signal generator, and use your oscilloscope to meas-ure its frequency response in the range 10 c/s to 10 kc/s. Plot this response (i) on linear graph paper, (ii) on 3 decade semi-logarithmic paper, first converting output voltage to decibels. Compare this curve with the theoretical curve given in this chapter.

2. Using a square wave generator and your oscilloscope, measure the time constant of the filter. Compare this with the calculated time constant. From the time constant, calculate f_0, and compare this with the measured value obtained from the 3 db point in question 1 above. What is the rise time?

3. Measure and plot on semi-logarithmic paper the high-frequency response of your oscilloscope (a) with the gain control at maximum, (b) with the gain control set half-way up. Explain any difference between these two curves. Is the Y amplifier circuit a simple 6 db per octave filter? What is its rise time?

4. If an electrocardiograph is available, run the chart at the maximum speed available, and abruptly apply an input of 1 mV. (The voltage calibrator constructed in Chapter 1 is ideal for this purpose; otherwise the calibration facility built into the instrument may be used.) Read off the rise time from your record, and compare it with the value given in Table 20.1 at the end of Chapter 20. If you are familiar with clinical electrocardiography, consider in what way an ECG waveform would be distorted by an amplifier with inadequate high-frequency response (excessive rise time). In what way would this distortion be clini-cally significant?

CHAPTER 20

LOW-FREQUENCY RESPONSE

20.1. HIGH-PASS FILTER

A high-pass filter allows high frequencies to pass, but attenuates low frequencies. The simplest and most important type is the RC network shown in Fig. 20.1.

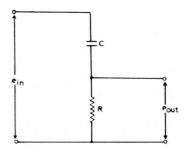

FIG. 20.1. Simple high-pass filter.

As in Chapter 19, the total impedance Z_{total} is given by

$$Z_{total} = \sqrt{(R^2 + Z_c^2)},$$

but now the output of the voltage divider is given by

$$e_{out} = \frac{R}{Z_{total}} \cdot e_{in} \tag{20.1}$$

and the gain is given by

$$G = \frac{R}{Z_{total}} = \frac{R}{\sqrt{(R^2 + Z_C^2)}}$$

$$= \frac{1}{\sqrt{(R^2 + Z_C^2)/R^2}}$$

$$= \frac{1}{\sqrt{[(Z_C^2/R^2) + 1]}}. \tag{20.2}$$

As in the case of the low-pass filter, at some frequency f_o, $Z_c = R$, and again

136

the gain is 0·707. Also, as before,

$$f_0 = \frac{1}{2\pi RC},$$

and this represents the 3 db point, but now this is a lower frequency limit. The general curve for a high-pass filter is given in Fig. 20.2. The curve again falls at 6 db per octave, but with the slope reversed.

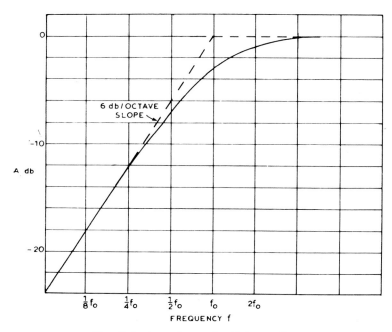

FIG. 20.2. General curve for high-pass filter.

High-pass filters are used in biological amplifiers to remove interfering signals of lower frequency than the ones being observed, for example, to remove slow skin potential changes from an ECG. As in the low-pass case, two or more filters may be cascaded to increase the rate of attenuation.

It will be realised that a condenser coupling between two stages of amplification constitutes a high-pass filter, in conjunction with the output resistance of the first stage and the input resistance of the second stage; the cut-off frequency of the coupling may readily be calculated by the method given above.

It is fortunate that mechanical recording systems have no such limitations; the frequency response extends down to zero.

The transient response of a high-pass filter can be readily deduced. If an abrupt 1 V step is applied to the input of Fig. 20.3, the condenser will initially remain uncharged, and the full 1 V will appear across R and the output. As the condenser charges exponentially, it will take more and more of the 1 V, leaving less and less across R and the output; the output will fall exponentially to zero with a time constant of RC.

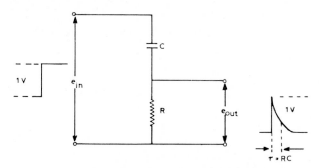

FIG. 20.3. Transient response of high-pass filter.

It will be clear that if only a short rectangular pulse is applied to the filter, the output voltage will not have fallen much by the time the pulse terminates, and the result will be as in Fig. 20.4.

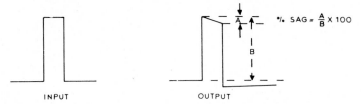

FIG. 20.4. Output of high-pass filter with time constant long compared with applied pulse.

The distortion produced is generally expressed as percentage *sag* in the top of the pulse. The initial part of the decay is approximately linear, and if it continued at this rate would fall to zero in one time constant; so the approximate rule holds that the percentage sag is equal to the percentage of a time constant occupied by the pulse. For example, if the time constant is 1 sec, a pulse of 0·01 sec duration would have 1% sag. Conversely, if a pulse of 100 msec is to be passed with not more than 5% sag by a certain coupling, the coupling time constant must be at least 20 times 100 msec or 2 sec. For low

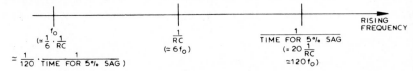

FIG. 20.5. Relations between cut-off frequency, 5% sag time, and time constant for a simple high-pass filter.

frequencies, the relationship between f_0 and the time constant can be summarised by Fig. 20.5.

If the filter time constant is made very short compared with the pulse duration, a rectangular pulse will be reproduced as in Fig. 20.6.

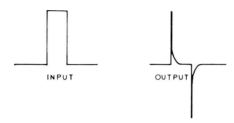

INPUT   OUTPUT

FIG. 20.6. Differentiation of pulse.

This effect has already been mentioned in §16.7; the output is an approximation to the differential of the input, and the filter is sometimes loosely described as a differentiating circuit.

20.2. FREQUENCY RANGE OF BIOELECTRIC SIGNALS

Table 20.1 shows the frequency range required for accurate reproduction of various types of bioelectric signal. For any particular type, use of apparatus with a range in excess of this will merely increase the thermal agitation noise (Chapter 2) and other spurious signals produced by the amplifier or the source of signal. Biological amplifiers are frequently provided with a switched selection of high- and low-pass filters to limit the frequency range to that required. On the other hand, some reduction in the range given in the table can often be tolerated, particularly when the apparatus is used for diagnostic purposes only. The ultimate test is, of course, whether the waveform being examined is degraded in a clinically significant fashion.

TABLE 20.1.

FREQUENCY RANGE OF BIOELECTRIC SIGNALS

Type of potential	Upper limit		Lower limit	
	3 db point	Rise time	3 db point	Time for 5 % sag
EMG, nerve action potential	6 kc/s	60 μsec	2 c/s	4 msec
Phonocardiography	1000 c/s	350 μsec	0·5 c/s	16 msec
Pulse pressure recording	50 c/s	7 msec	0·2 c/s	40 msec
ECG	150 c/s	2·3 msec	0·03 c/s	280 msec
EEG	50 c/s	7 msec	0·05 c/s	160 msec

Further reading

As for Chapter 19.

PRACTICAL

1. Set up a simple RC high-pass filter, using $R = 33$ K, $C = 0.01$, as in Fig. 20.2. Drive it from an audio-signal generator, and use your oscilloscope to measure its frequency response. Plot this response on semi-logarithmic paper, first converting output voltages to decibels. Compare this curve with the theoretical curve given in this chapter.

2. Using a square wave generator and your oscilloscope, measure the percentage sag of your high-pass filter response in a known time, and hence derive the measured time constant. Compare this with the calculated value. From this value, derive f_0, and compare it with the value obtained from the 3 db point in question 1 above.

3. Set up the transistor amplifier assembled in Chapter 9, and plot its low-frequency response curve on semi-logarithmic paper. What is f_0? From this value, derive the input time constant, and hence deduce the input resistance of the amplifier.

4. If an electrocardiograph is available, run the chart at standard recording speed (2·5 cm/sec) and apply an input of 1 mV for about 1 sec. (The voltage calibrator constructed in Chapter 1 is ideal for this purpose.) From your record, read off the percentage sag in a known time, and compare it with the value given in Table 20.1 at the end of this chapter. If you are familiar with clinical electrocardiography, consider in what way an ECG waveform would be distorted by an amplifier with inadequate low-frequency response (excessive sag). In what way would this distortion be clinically significant?

CHAPTER 21

RECORDING FROM TISSUE

21.1. INTRODUCTION

Two difficulties arise in the recording of electrical activity in tissue. One is in the provision of a suitable electrode system for connecting the measuring equipment to the tissue; the other is in recording the desired activity in the presence of other activity and of signals extraneous to the tissue. These problems will be considered in turn.

21.2. ELECTRODE SYSTEMS

The conduction of currents in tissue, as in any other liquid system, is purely electrolytic; that is to say, by the migration of positive and negative ions from point to point. To measure electrical effects in tissue it is necessary to make a transfer from electrolytic conduction to the electronic conduction which occurs in the measuring circuit, and this can be done only by means of a pair of electrodes which are reversible, in the electrochemical sense. For biological purposes the most usual electrodes are made of silver, coated with a film of solid silver chloride. In a chloride-containing solution there is a very small but finite concentration of silver ions in the vicinity of the silver electrode. If such an electrode is made negative to the solution, as in Fig. 21.1a, silver ions pass on to the surface of the silver electrode, taking up their place on the silver crystalline lattice, and accepting an electron each. A correspond-

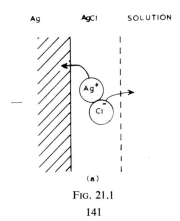

Ag   AgCl   SOLUTION

(a)

FIG. 21.1

141

ing amount of solid silver chloride passes into solution, releasing chloride ions into the bulk of the solution to carry the current. If the electrode is made positive to the solution, as in Fig. 21.1b,

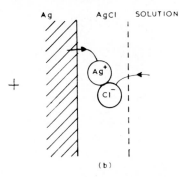

FIG. 21.1. Silver-silver chloride electrode. (a) As cathode. (b) As anode.

silver atoms pass from the crystalline lattice into solution as ions, each relinquishing an electron as it does. Chloride ions arrive from the bulk solution, carrying the current, and precipitate with the silver ions as solid silver chloride. The composite electrode, in fact, behaves as a system *reversible to chloride*. If a pair of such electrodes is used, no net work is required to pass a current from metal to solution to metal in either direction and consequently no spurious potentials are added to the system.

A suitable film of silver chloride may be built up on a clean silver surface by making it positive to a chloride-containing solution, and passing a current of about 1 mA/cm² for several minutes.

For electrocardiography, zinc electrodes are probably the most suitable; these form a chloride-reversible surface in the same way that silver electrodes do. However, for aesthetic reasons it is more usual to find stainless steel or chrome-plated brass electrodes. These electrodes are irreversible. If such an electrode is made negative to a solution, a current will flow only if it is sufficiently negative (about 2 V) to cause hydrogen to be discharged on its surface. If it is made positive, a current will flow only if it is sufficiently positive (about 0·6 V) to discharge oxygen on its surface. For measuring purposes this means that spurious potentials (due, for example, to dissolved oxygen) are introduced, and these in general will be slowly varying. If fairly rapidly varying signals, such as the ECG or EEG, are to be recorded, these slowly varying components can be removed with a high-pass filter. If slowly varying signals, such as smooth muscle potentials from the abdomen, are to be recorded, reversible electrodes are essential. Steel or tungsten electrodes are common for electromyography and as implanted brain electrodes; although they are necessary for mechanical reasons, it must be realised that they are irreversible.

21.3. RECORDING FROM A BULK MEDIUM

A living cell in the resting state maintains its cytoplasm at a potential negative to its surroundings, and of the order of 40–80 mV. If some region of the cell is activated, this region rapidly loses its potential and, in most cases, reverses it. This causes a current to flow into the active region from adjacent ones, which causes them to be activated in turn. It is this current in the external medium which may be detected by a suitable electrode system. Consider, for example, a skeletal muscle fibre, shown diagrammatically in Fig. 21.2.

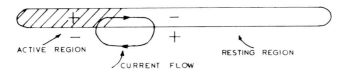

FIG. 21.2. Activated region in living cell.

Such a fibre can at any instant be idealised as a *dipole*, a paired source of current and sink of current a little distance apart. For simplicity, consider a dipole of strength 10 V, in a three-dimensional conducting medium, as shown in Fig. 21.3.

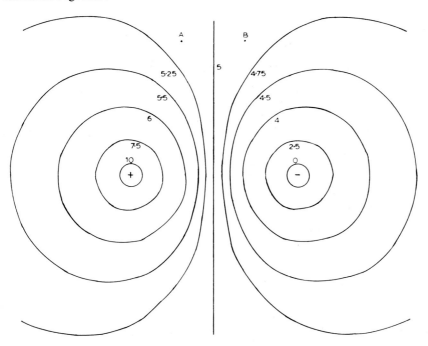

FIG. 21.3. Current dipole in conducting medium.

By the use of a probe electrode, equipotential surfaces can be plotted out, and a cross-section of these surfaces in the plane of the paper is shown in the diagram. It will be noticed that the potentials fall off very rapidly in the vicinity of the source and sink, and quite slowly elsewhere. A pair of measuring electrodes inserted at points A and B, for example, would record only about $\frac{1}{4}$ V between them. The lines of current flow from source to sink will be everywhere at right angles to the equipotentials, following the potential gradients.

In the case of the living cell, the strength and position of the dipole vary from instant to instant, and so, of course, does the field pattern. If a pair of electrodes is inserted in the tissue, the two electrodes will in general be on different equipotentials, and will record the difference between them; this is *bipolar* recording. It can be shown that the recorded potential difference will fall off approximately inversely as the square of distance from the dipole.

A second method of recording is *monopolar*, in which case one electrode is placed far out from the dipole, and the other in proximity to it. It will be clear from the equipotential diagram that the remote (or *indifferent*) electrode must be very close to the mean potential of source and sink (here 5 V) no matter where it is placed, so long as it is far out. The probe electrode will then record the difference between itself and the mean. In general this gives a larger potential than bipolar recording, but the potential falls off approximately inversely with distance from the dipole; if more remote groups of cells are active, they may affect the record obtained. This may or may not be desirable.

21.4. REJECTION OF EXTERNAL INTERFERENCE

Consider a human patient lying on a couch, as in Fig. 21.4, to allow an

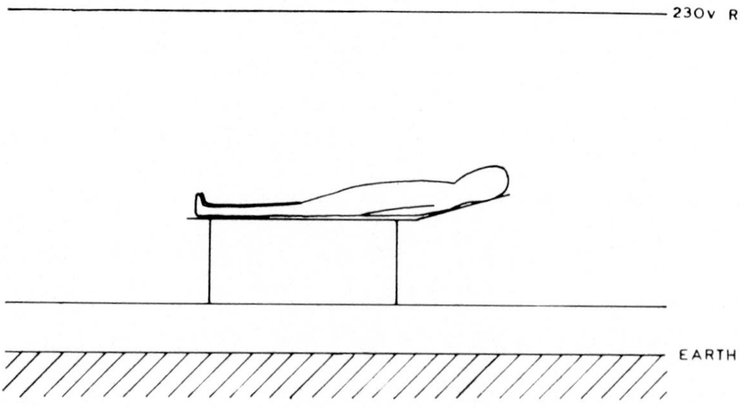

FIG. 21.4. Patient in AC field.

:lectrocardiagram to be taken. There will be AC supply wiring at various ـoints in the floor, walls and ceiling, and in modern practice this is usually ـnshielded. For simplicity, consider an active lead in the ceiling alone.

The patient is clearly between the plates of a condenser (the wire and earth) ـo which an alternating voltage is applied. If he were half-way between ـhem, he would assume an alternating potential of 115 V RMS! Of course, ـhe capacitance is quite small, so only a very small current can be drawn ـrom him without reducing this potential greatly; but without suitable pre-ـautions it will cause intolerable interference with a recording of a bioelectric ـotential. The removal or shielding of all wiring is impracticable. The use of ـ screened room, which forms a Faraday cage, is possible for laboratory work, ـut quite unsuitable generally.

Two ingenious solutions of this problem are in common use. Consider an ـdealised spherical patient, as in Fig. 21.5, with a pair of applied recording ـlectrodes.

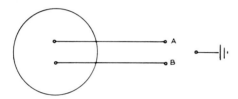

FIG. 21.5. Patient and recording electrode.

ـhe desired signal is that from *A* to *B*, but in addition both *A* and *B* have a ـarge undesired signal with respect to earth. These two components are ـeferred to as the out-of-phase and the in-phase signal respectively. The in-ـhase signal would not matter, of course, if the recording equipment had ـbsolutely no connection to earth, but this is not usually possible, since it ـnust be supplied with AC power.

(i) If a suitable transformer were available, it could be connected as in Fig. ـ1.6.

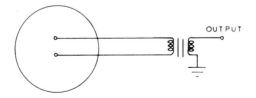

FIG. 21.6. Patient isolating transformer.

ـn this case only the out-of-phase signal would appear in the output, since ـnly the out-of-phase signal would cause primary current to flow. However, it is not possible to construct such a transformer for the low frequencies involved in an ECG or EEG; but by first converting the signal to a higher frequency range (using it to *modulate* a *carrier* frequency) the system becomes practicable.

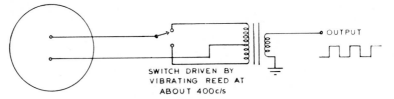

SWITCH DRIVEN BY
VIBRATING REED AT
ABOUT 400c/s

OUTPUT

FIG. 21.7. Chopper modulator and transformer.

A simple arrangement to do this is shown in Fig. 21.7. A constant potential between the electrodes of Fig. 21.6 would give a constant primary current, and so no secondary voltage. If this current is periodically reversed by a rapidly vibrating switch, a rectangular wave of voltage will appear at the output, with an amplitude accurately proportional to the original electrode potential difference. This can then be amplified and subsequently rectified, to give an amplified reproduction of the original signal. This system is quite common for frequencies up to about 100 c/s, so it is suitable for ECG and EEG recording, and for other relatively low-frequency signals.

(ii) A balanced amplifier may be used to reject in-phase signals, while giving normal amplification to out-of-phase ones. A balanced amplifier as used to drive the deflecting plates of a CRT has already been encountered in Chapter 13. As used for in-phase signal rejection, the circuit is as shown in Fig. 21.8. This circuit is variously called a differential, balanced or long-tailed pair amplifier.

Consider first an out-of-phase signal of 1 V appearing between the electrodes. This will appear on one grid as a signal of $+0.5$ V, and on the other as -0.5 V, with respect to earth. If the upper grid moves positively, the plate current of the upper valve rises; at the same time the lower grid moves negatively, and the plate current of the lower valve falls by the same amount. The net current through the common cathode resistor (the "long tail") remains unchanged, and each valve amplifies as though it were acting alone, with its cathode earthed. Assuming a stage gain of 40, the upper plate will fall 20 V, and the lower plate rise 20 V.

Now consider an in-phase signal of $+0.5$ V, appearing at each electrode simultaneously with respect to earth. The plate current of each valve will rise, causing the net current through the common cathode resistor to rise. In fact the two valves together behave rather as a cathode follower, the cathode voltage rising almost as much as the grids. This will mean that each plate falls by about 0.5 V also. At the output there is no out-of-phase voltage, and no amplification of the original in-phase input.

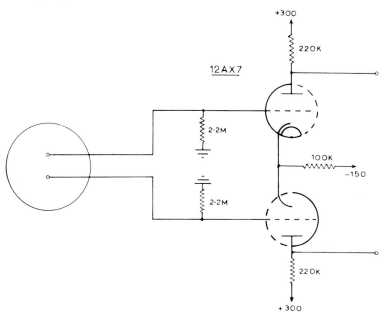

FIG. 21.8. Differential amplifier.

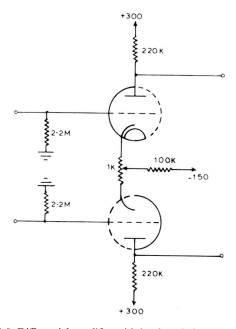

FIG. 21.9. Differential amplifier with in-phase balance potentiometer.

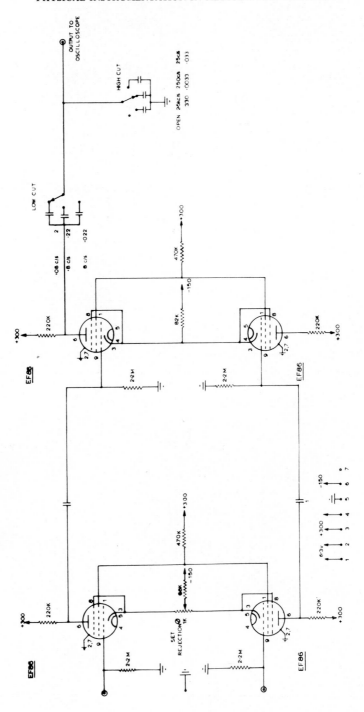

FIG. 21.10. Biological preamplifier circuit.

The foregoing has assumed perfect balance between the two halves of the circuit. In fact the two valves may differ by 10% or more in respect of either μ, r_p, or both, but fortunately this may be corrected by the use of a balancing potentiometer in the cathode, as shown in Fig. 21.9.

This reduces the gain of each valve somewhat when the contact is central; as it is moved, the gain of one valve is raised and the other lowered, until balance is obtained, and no out-of-phase output occurs for an in-phase input.

The *rejection ratio* of a balanced amplifier is defined as the ratio of *out-of-phase output for a given out-of-phase input* to *out-of-phase output for the same given input applied in-phase*. It should ideally be infinite; in practice a figure of 10,000 is desirable, and can readily be obtained.

Either triodes or pentodes can be used in a balanced amplifier, depending on the gain desired. Pentodes are used in the preamplifier to be constructed in the practical session; the screens are fed from a common resistor, giving additional balancing.

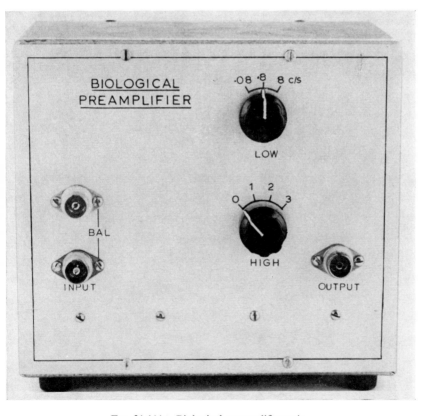

FIG. 21.11(a). Biological preamplifier unit.

The input resistance of an amplifier used for recording from tissue should be large compared with the electrode resistance, to prevent loss of signal amplitude, and what is worse, loss of rejection if the two electrode resistances are unequal. A minimum of 2 M is desirable for ordinary ECG or EEG electrodes; a higher value may well be used for EMG or implanted brain electrodes. This requirement almost precludes the use of transistors in the input stages of biological amplifiers, in the present state of their development. They are, of course, quite suitable following a chopper modulator and transformer.

Further Reading

DONALDSON, *Electronic Apparatus for Biological Research*, Butterworth, London, 1958.
MIT Radiation Laboratory Series, vol. 18, p. 441, McGraw-Hill, New York, 1948.
DEWHURST, *Electronic Engineering*, **31**, 355 (1959).
KLEIN AND ZAALBERG VAN ZELST, *Philips Technical Review*, **22**, 345 (1960/61).
KLEIN AND ZAALBERG VAN ZELST, *Philips Technical Review*, **23**, 142 (1961/62).
KAY, *Experimental Biology*, Chapman and Hall, London, 1964.
BURES, PETRAN AND ZACHAR, *Electrophysiological Methods*, Czechoslovak Academy of Sciences, Prague, 1960.

FIG. 21.11(b). Biological preamplifier: upper view.

FIG. 21.11(c). Biological preamplifier: lower view.

PRACTICAL

Construct the two stage biological preamplifier shown in the circuit of Figs. 21.10 and the photographs of Fig. 21.11. Omit the output filters for the time being. Connect the output to your oscilloscope, and set the rejection control for optimum rejection of an in-phase signal. Calibrate it to give 1 mV per centimetre of screen deflection, and use it to examine an ECG.

CHAPTER 22

TISSUE STIMULATION

22.1. INTRODUCTION

Electrical stimulation of tissue is a valuable test of its ability to perform its normal function. Although synaptic transmission from one nerve cell to another is chemical, the propagation of excitation in any individual nerve cell is electrical, and can be initiated by a suitable electrical stimulus. This in turn initiates contraction in muscle and secretion in gland tissue.

22.2. MODE OF ACTION

Excitation of a living cell is brought about by an outward current of sufficient magnitude. What must be achieved is, in fact, the depletion of ions at the cell boundary. If a large current is passed for a short time this will be achieved; as the current is reduced, diffusion replaces the ions removed by the current to a greater and greater extent, and more and more charge must pass to achieve depletion. Finally, a lower limit of current is reached, below which excitation will not occur, no matter how long the current is maintained. For any given tissue a strength–duration curve may be drawn, which will have the form of Fig. 22.1.

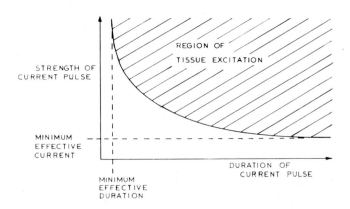

FIG. 22.1. Tissue strength-duration curve.

Following nerve injury, the form of this curve for a muscle may be prognostic. The velocity of propagation of excitation in a nerve or muscle depends on its diameter, the type of tissue, and its condition. Thus measurement of conduction velocity is frequently used diagnostically.

22.3. TISSUE RESISTANCE

It is obviously desirable in many cases to stimulate a nerve or muscle through the skin; in this case much of the total current flow will occur through regions other than the one aimed at. Accordingly, the actual value of current which flows has no real significance; but the shape of the strength–duration curve has. Dry skin offers a considerable resistance to current flow. This may be minimised by the use of electrodes of considerable area, and by rubbing the skin with a liberal coating of electrode jelly. (Note that surgical lubricant jellies are quite unsuitable, being reasonably good insulators.) ECG electrodes can offer a resistance of the order of 1 K–3 K with suitable preparation. Much lower resistance will be encountered once the skin boundary has been passed; a cubic centimetre of tissue has a resistance of about 150 ohm between opposite faces. Many stimulators are calibrated in volts, but, in fact, have so great an internal resistance that if a piece of moist tissue is connected to them, only a fraction of the rated voltage appears.

22.4. STIMULUS PULSE WAVEFORMS

A rectangular pulse of voltage is frequently used in experimental measurements. This allows results obtained by different workers to be compared, but still only provided that the electrode resistance and placement are the same in all cases. For many purposes, a simpler waveform to use is the exponentially decaying pulse produced by discharging a condenser of suitable size through the tissue, or by applying a step of voltage through a transformer. The obsolete terminology of "galvanic" for stimulation by a pulse of DC, and "faradic" for stimulation by a pulse induced in the secondary of a transformer is still occasionally used.

22.5. STIMULUS ISOLATION UNITS

It is often required to stimulate a piece of tissue, such as a nerve or muscle, at one point, and to record the propagated impulse at another. If one of the stimulating electrodes is earthed, the stimulus pulse appears at the recording electrodes as a very large in-phase signal, which may easily be sufficient to produce an intolerable "stimulus artefact" in the final record. Although the stimulus pulse is usually over before the propagated impulse reaches the recording electrodes, the disturbance in the amplifier and recording system which it produces can easily persist sufficiently long to obscure the desired record. This effect can be overcome by the use of a *stimulus isolation circuit* at the output of the stimulator, so arranged that it has no direct connection to earth and a minimum of capacitance to earth. It is possible to use a specially designed transformer for this purpose, but these are bulky, expensive and tend to distort the stimulus pulse. More commonly a rectangular pulse of voltage is used to turn an oscillator on and off. The output of this can be fed through a simple isolating transformer, then rectified and either used directly, or better, used to turn a battery on and off to provide the

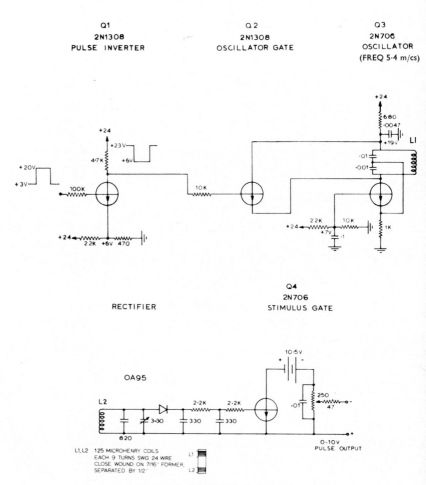

FIG. 22.2. Stimulus isolation unit.

stimulus. A suitable circuit for this purpose is shown in Fig. 22.2. The incoming rectangular pulse of the desired duration is inverted in Q1, and used to turn Q2 on and off. If Q2 is off, the oscillator Q3 runs freely. If Q2 is on, it acts as a short circuit across the tank circuit of Q3, and stops oscillation. If Q3 is oscillating, it induces an alternating voltage in the transformer secondary; this is rectified, filtered and used to turn Q4 on. If Q4 is on, about 10·3 V appears across the 250 ohm potentiometer, and any convenient fraction can be selected as a stimulus. In the absence of oscillation in Q3, there is no bias on Q4 and it is cut off; there is thus no voltage at the output.

22.6. CARDIAC DEFIBRILLATORS

Due to a variety of causes, including accidental electrocution, the human heart can commence ventricular fibrillation. In this state, individual portions of the ventricular muscle contract independently instead of synchronously and effective output of blood ceases; death follows rapidly. If immediate action is taken it is possible to correct this condition by the application of a suitable powerful electrical stimulus to the heart. A typical cardiac defibrillator for this purpose consists of a large high-voltage condenser, which is charged to several thousand volts by means of an EHT circuit similar in principle to that of Chapter 12. It is then discharged through the heart by means of large electrodes applied to the chest wall. Shocks of 200–400 joules are common in this application.

Further Reading

DONALDSON, *Electronic Apparatus for Biological Research*, Butterworth, London, 1958.
KAY, *Experimental Biology*, Chapman & Hall, London, 1964.
Medical Research Council, *Peripheral Nerve Injuries*, Her Majesty's Stationery Office, London, 1954.

PRACTICAL

1. Complete the preamplifier under construction by the addition of the switched high- and low-pass filters. Using your oscilloscope and test pulse generator, measure the overall percentage sag of the system for each switch position of the low-frequency filter. Similarly, measure the rise time for each position of the high-frequency filter. Using a sine-wave generator, plot the frequency response for each switch position.

2. Record an ECG on the oscilloscope and sketch the effect on the waveform of each position of each filter.

3. The construction of any available stimulators and stimulus isolation units should be examined, and the output waveforms investigated on a suitable oscilloscope.

CHAPTER 23

GEIGER COUNTER, RATEMETER

23.1. DETECTION OF RADIATION

The presence of a radioactive source may be detected by means of a suitable device capable of responding to high-energy electrons. The types of radiation normally encountered are beta and gamma. Beta radiation, which is in fact a stream of high energy electrons, is detected directly. It is characterised by a relatively short range in air, and is readily stopped by quite thin sheets of material. Gamma radiation, which is identical with X-radiation, is detected by the fact that it produces secondary electrons, largely by collision with the walls of the detector, and these are then measured. It is characterised by long range and penetrating power.

Two general types of detector are in common use; the Geiger-Müller tube is dealt with in this chapter, and the scintillation counter is treated in Chapter 24. The latter is considerably more sensitive.

The Geiger tube consists of a metal cylinder, through the axis of which passes a thin wire which is maintained at a high positive potential with respect to the cylinder. The cylinder is filled with a mixture of argon with alcohol or halogen vapour, at reduced pressure. For gamma counting, the cylinder is closed off with end plates; for beta counting, one end is made of thin mica or aluminium foil. The tube is coupled to an amplifier through a condenser, as shown in Fig. 23.1.

An electron passing through the tube collides with atoms of the gas filling, releasing outer shell electrons. These are accelerated towards the central wire, and in turn produce further ionisation by collision. On collection by the central wire, the free electrons give rise to a flow of current through the load resistor, and a change of potential at the amplifier input. There would be a cumulative rise in current if the tube were not *quenched*; this is the function of the alcohol or halogen filling. In its presence a pulse of current flows for each particle that enters. In a correctly operated Geiger tube, the pulse height is independent of the energy of the original particle entering the tube. After the production of a pulse, a period of 100 or 200 μsec is required for recovery before the tube can detect a further pulse; this is the *paralysis time*. A correction for counting time lost in this manner can readily be calculated for any measured counting rate. Since paralysis time of a tube depends on rather variable factors, an artificial "paralysis time" rather longer than that anticipated is usually introduced into the associated amplifier if quantitative counting of samples is required.

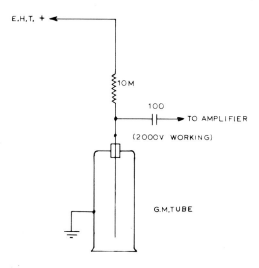

FIG. 23.1. Geiger tube and output circuit.

If the EHT voltage is slowly raised from zero while the tube is exposed to constant radiation, a curve of the form shown in Fig. 23.2 will be obtained. The plateau region is the one used for operation. Its position and length depend on the type of tube used, and these figures are usually indicated on each individual tube or in the relevant data. The plateau voltage must not be exceeded or the tube will be destroyed.

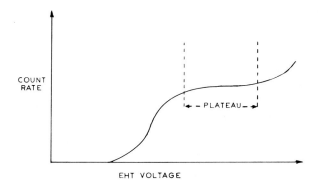

FIG. 23.2. Characteristic curve of Geiger tube.

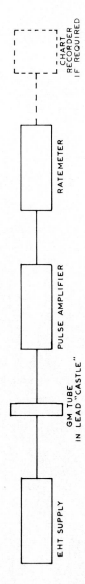

FIG. 23.3. Geiger counter with ratemeter.

23.2. BACKGROUND

In the absence of a deliberately introduced source, a counter will always indicate a low but definite count rate. This is due in part to cosmic radiation, in part to radiation due to natural causes and traces of nuclear fallout, and possibly also to contamination of the counting equipment or the adjacent bench. Regular checks should be made of this background level, which is subtracted from each actual count made. It may be minimised by lead shielding about the Geiger tube, and by scrupulous care to avoid any spills.

23.3. EQUIPMENT FOR GEIGER COUNTING

A simple unit for detection of radioactive contamination by a *gamma* source will be constructed in the practical session. For quantitative work, two methods of measurement of the count rate, which is proportional to the *amount* of isotope present, are in general use. For quick measurements of low accuracy, a ratemeter is used. This arrangement will be discussed in the next section. For higher accuracy, a scaler is necessary. Details of this instrument will be discussed in Chapter 24; it is equally applicable to Geiger and to scintillation counting. A typical layout of equipment using a ratemeter is shown in Fig. 23.3.

Suitable "building blocks" for all types of instrumentation are made by many manufacturers.

23.4. THE "DIODE PUMP" RATEMETER

Pulses from the Geiger tube are quite small. They are amplified up to several volts, and are then used to trigger a monostable multivibrator; this produces a rectangular pulse of constant height and duration for each incoming pulse. The rectangular pulses are fed to a *diode pump circuit*; a typical arrangement is shown in Fig. 23.4.

This shows a monostable pulse generator, emitter follower driver stage, and diode pump circuit, with values of C1, C2 and C3 suitable for a range of 0–100 pulses per second on the meter. On the arrival of a pulse, the mono-stable multivibrator is triggered, and the emitter of Q3 moves from zero to about -6 V. This causes C2 to charge to this voltage through D1. At the end of this monostable delay period, which is determined by C1, the emitter of Q3 returns to zero. Since C2 cannot abruptly change its state of charge, point A is carried positively. D2 conducts and the charge on C2 is shared with C3. Since C3 is much larger than C2, it takes almost the whole of the charge, and C2 practically empties into it. So for a succession of pulses the voltage of

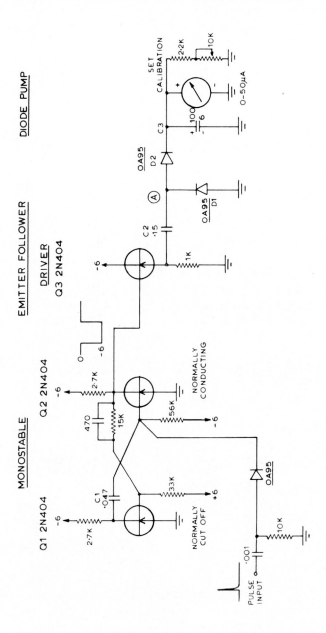

FIG. 23.4. Diode pump circuit for 0–100 pulses per second.

C3 is "pumped up" in a series of small steps. However, its charge is continually leaking away through the meter and its shunt (the "set calibration" control), and as the voltage rises this leakage rises also until a steady state is reached, at a meter current depending on the rate at which the original pulses are arriving.

Each incoming pulse of voltage e_{in} charges C2 by an amount

$$Q = C_2 \cdot e_{in} \quad \text{(Chapter 2)}$$

and if f pulses per second are arriving,

$$\text{charge/sec} = fQ = fC_2e_{in}.$$

But charge/sec is by definition current, so

$$i_{in} = fC_2e_{in}.$$

In the steady state, this must be equal to the current through the meter and its shunt, so

$$f = \frac{i_{meter}}{C_2e_{in}}. \qquad (23.1)$$

Notice that this expression does not contain either the value of C3 or the meter resistance; the time constant $C_3 \cdot R_{meter}$ merely determines the response time of the system. If this is too long, the meter will be sluggish in responding to changes in rate; if it is too short, the meter pointer will flicker about the mean reading, particularly at low pulse rates.

If a permanent record of pulse rate is required, a suitable recording microammeter may be substituted for the meter.

Diode pump ratemeters are frequently used, not only for muscular counting, but also as frequency meters, revolution ratemeters, and cardiotachometers and respiration ratemeters.

23.5. EHT SUPPLIES

EHT supplies are usually generated by a high-frequency oscillator, as was described in Chapter 12. A typical transistor oscillator is shown in the practical session. This differs in operation from the valve oscillator described previously only in the fact that the ferrite core of the transformer saturates in each cycle, and the output waveform is consequently a series of sharp positive pulses rather than a sine wave; however, the efficiency of transformation is high. A voltage doubler circuit of somewhat unorthodox design is employed, to make full use of the sharp waveform. C1 charges to the peak value of the transformer voltage, which is 250 V, through D1. C2 then charges to +250 V through the 1 M resistor, with its lower plate positive to its upper one. Each succeeding transformer pulse takes its upper plate to +250, so its lower plate lifts to +500. Since the lower plate of C3 is at +250 V, this charges C3 to +250 V through D2. C3 and C1 are in series, giving +500 V output. Since operation anywhere in the plateau region is satisfactory, extreme EHT stability is not required for Geiger counting.

Further Reading

Rossi and Staub, *Ionisation Chambers and Counters*, McGraw-Hill, New York, 1949.

Elmore and Sands, *Electronics*, McGraw-Hill, New York, 1949.

Selected Semiconductor Circuits, MIL-HDBK-215, US Government Printing Office, 1960.

Radioactive Materials and Stable Isotopes, AERE, Harwell, 1957.

Meloan and Kiser, *Instrumental Analysis*, Merrill, Columbus, Ohio, 1963.

PRACTICAL

1. Construct the emitter follower and Geiger tube section of your gamma radiation detector, using the circuit of Fig. 23.5, and the photographs of Fig. 23.6. Check the output DC level of the emitter follower.

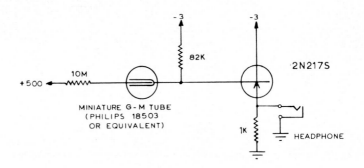

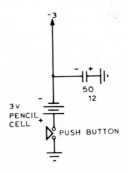

Fig. 23.5. Gamma radiation detector—counter section.

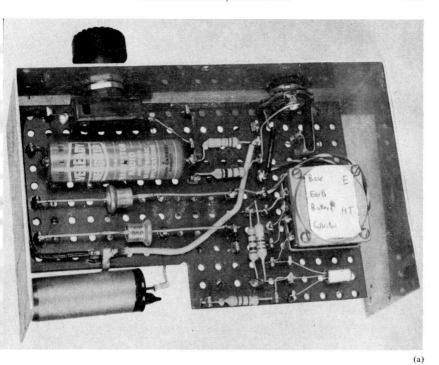

(a)

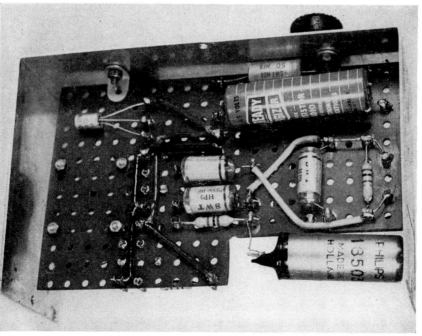

(b)

FIG. 23.6. Gamma radiation detector. (a) Left. (b) Right.

2. Complete the gamma radiation detector by constructing its EHT supply, according to the circuit of Fig. 23.7. Test it on the luminous dial of a watch, and on a source of gamma radiation. Test the effectiveness of a lead brick as a radiation shield.

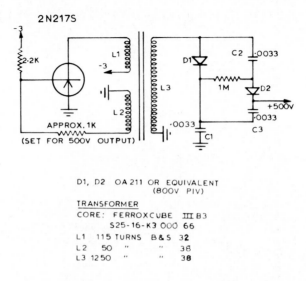

D1, D2   OA 211 OR EQUIVALENT
(800V PIV)

TRANSFORMER
CORE: FERROXCUBE III B3
         S25-16-K3 000 66
L1   115 TURNS B&S 32
L2   50   "   "   38
L3 1250   "   "   38

FIG. 23.7. Gamma radiation detector—EHT supply.

3. The pumping action of a diode pump ratemeter may be observed on an oscilloscope by use of the circuit of Fig. 23.8.

4. The features of any available Geiger tubes, Geiger counters and ratemeters should be examined.

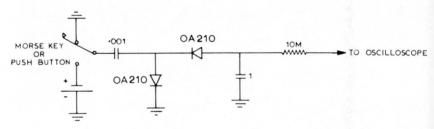

FIG. 23.8. Demonstration of diode pump circuit.

TYPICAL RULES FOR A RADIOCHEMICAL LABORATORY

1. To avoid accidental ingestion of radioactive isotopes, smoking and eating are not permitted in the laboratory, and the hands should be kept away from the mouth.

2. Fluids must be pipetted by means of a syringe, *never* by mouth.

3. A film badge must be worn at all times when in the radioisotope section of the laboratory.

4. Glassware used for manipulation of radioisotopes must not be removed from the radioisotope section until it has been monitored by a beta or gamma counter, depending on the isotope in use, and passed as free of contamination.

5. All manipulations must be carried out on several thicknesses of filter paper. Any spills whatsoever, however small, must be reported.

6. At the end of a manipulation all active materials must be disposed of as directed for the isotope concerned, and the working area and the operator's hands monitored for possible activity.

7. Radioisotopes not actually being manipulated, particularly gamma emitters, must be kept behind a barrier of lead bricks.

CHAPTER 24

SCINTILLATION COUNTER, SCALER

24.1. SCINTILLATION COUNTER

The scintillation counter depends on the fact that a flash of visible light is produced when an electron or burst of gamma radiation passes into a suitable phosphor; this phenomenon has already been discussed in connection with cathode ray tube screens. Solid phosphors for scintillation counting consist of large crystals of activated sodium iodide, or of substances such as anthracene or stilbene dispersed in a transparent solid medium, such as Perspex; alternatively, they can be dissolved in toluene or similar solvents. Under suitable conditions the phosphor can actually be added to the radioactive liquid to be counted. Each flash of light, normally in the blue region, is "seen" by a photomultiplier tube. This consists of a light-sensitive cathode, which emits electrons when illuminated, and a chain of *dynodes* at progressively higher voltages, terminating in an anode, as shown diagrammatically in Fig. 24.1.

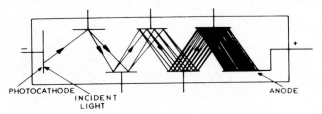

FIG. 24.1. Principle of photomultiplier.

An electron emitted from the cathode is attracted to the first dynode, which it hits with sufficient energy to expel several secondary electrons (up to about 10). These in turn are attracted to the second dynode, where each expels several electrons, and so on. The anode may finally collect many million electrons for each primary one emitted from the photocathode. A total working voltage of about 1000 divided between 8–14 dynodes, is usual. The sensitivity is governed directly by the applied voltage, so highly stable supplies are required for quantitative measurements. The amount of light produced by a particle incident on the phosphor, and hence the pulse height produced at the photomultiplier anode, is governed by the energy of the particle at

166

impact; hence it is possible to calibrate the system in terms of incident particle energy. This is described as *proportional counting.* (Contrast this with the Geiger tube output, which is independent of particle energy.)

The light output of a phosphor is extremely small; with all its multiplication the pulses produced at the tube output are often only a few millivolts high. The phosphor and tube are operated in total darkness, and *the tube will be instantly destroyed if a trace of room light is permitted to enter* while the EHT is on. Photomultiplier tubes are extremely expensive.

The pulse durations are very short, of the order of 100 nanoseconds (millimicroseconds).

24.2. LINEAR AMPLIFIER

To increase the pulses to a level at which they can be counted, considerable amplification is necessary. A preamplifier unit is connected close to the PM tube, and its output fed to a main amplifier. These amplifiers must have a very good high-frequency response to handle the very fast pulses, and a very good stability of gain, to permit calibration.

24.3. DISCRIMINATION AND PULSE HEIGHT ANALYSIS

The output of the linear amplifier may, of course, be counted directly, but a considerable reduction in background can be effected by the use of a *discriminator*, which will pass only those pulses which exceed a preset voltage. The circuit most commonly encountered is the *Schmitt trigger*. It is found in both transistor and valve versions. A typical circuit is given in Fig. 24.2.

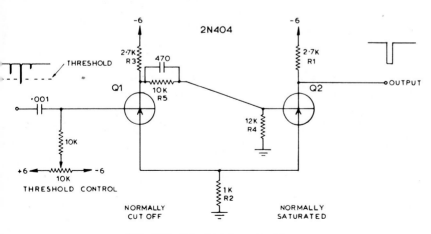

FIG. 24.2. Schmitt trigger circuit.

12a

This circuit is a variant on the multivibrator; one cross-coupling is orthodox, while the other is by means of the common emitter resistor R2. To understand its operation, ignore the input pulse for the moment, and consider only the effect of the threshold control. If this is set to $+6$ V, Q1 will be cut off. Its collector voltage will be nearly at -6 V, and this will saturate Q2 through the cross-coupling resistor R5. The current through Q2 will also flow through R2, and this will maintain the emitter of Q1 somewhat negative (at about -2 V, in the circuit of Fig. 24.2). As long as the base of Q1 is more positive than this, Q1 will remain cut off. If now the threshold control is moved negatively, nothing will happen until the base of Q1 reaches -2 V. At this point Q1 commences to conduct. Its collector moves positively, and this is transferred by means of R5 and R4 to move the base of Q2 positively. This reduces the current in Q2, and thus the voltage drop in R2, and the emitter voltage of Q1 moves positively. This reinforces the original change at the base of Q1; the action becomes cumulative, and the circuit abruptly flips over into a state in which Q1 is conducting and Q2 cut off. In doing so, the current through R2 has been reduced somewhat, and the circuit locks in this state. To restore it to its original condition, the threshold control must be moved positively until the current in Q1 falls enough to turn on Q2 by way of R5 and R4. When this occurs the circuit will abruptly trigger to the original state.

Suppose now the threshold control is left at say $+3$ V, and a series of negative pulses of various heights is fed into the input terminal. Only a pulse which exceeds 5 V in height $[3-(-2)]$ will be able to trigger the circuit. Immediately afterwards the pulse will die away, and will reset the circuit to its original state. Thus an output pulse of constant amplitude will appear corresponding to every pulse in excess of 5 V (the *threshold*); smaller pulses will produce no output. In practice the threshold control is calibrated directly in terms of threshold pulse height, and so can be used to measure pulse height. The output pulses from the Schmitt trigger are used to operate a ratemeter or counter.

If two radioisotopes producing particles of different energies are present, it may be possible by this means to count only the higher energy particles first, then both lots, and by subtraction to obtain the amount of each isotope present.

A more sophisticated technique for separation of two sets of pulses is pulse height analysis. In this method two discriminators are used, one being set at a threshold somewhat above the other. The two outputs enter an *anti-coincidence* circuit, which is so arranged that it produces no output if both discriminators fire simultaneously, but a pulse if only the lower one does. In the example shown in Fig. 24.3, all pulses between 3 and 4 V in height will produce an output pulse to the counting apparatus, but no others will be counted.

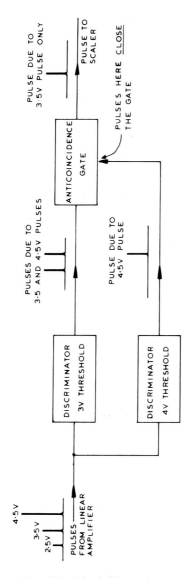

FIG. 24.3. Pulse height analyser.

24.4. SCALERS

For most work, the number of pulses in a given time or the time for a given number of pulses is actually measured. To do this at the high rates of counting frequently required, some type of electronic counter is needed. Early counters consisted of a long chain of bistable multivibrators, each acting as a "scale-of-two" to pass on one pulse for every two it received, and having in its plate circuit a small neon lamp to indicate whether it was flipped or not. By this means the total count was indicated in a binary scale of numbers; for example, a row of lamps would indicate units, twos, fours, eights, and so on, and all had to be added up to get the final decimal count. Thus if the shaded lamps on Fig. 24.4. were alight,

FIG. 24.4. Binary counting.

the count would be 53. A later refinement was to interlink the four multi-vibrators in a scale of 16 to force them to read in a decimal scale; this type of circuit, either with valves or transistors, is still in common use.

More common, however, is the use of special tubes which step round from zero to nine, and pass on a single pulse to the next decade each time they reset to zero. These may be either vacuum tubes with a heated cathode, as is the Philips EIT, or gas filled with a cold cathode, as is the Ericsson Dekatron. Both are somewhat limited as to maximum counting rate, and for high rates must be preceded by a chain of multivibrators or a high-speed decade tube such as the trochotron.

A complete scaler generally embodies an automatic timing circuit, so that a stop clock which is started at the same time as the scaler is automatically stopped after a preset number of counts.

24.5. STATISTICS OF COUNTING

Decay is a rare and random event, following a Poisson distribution. For a large frequency of events, this approaches a statistically normal distribution. Thus, if the same sample is counted a number of times under identical conditions, the number of counts obtained may be expected to vary, and the standard deviation of this variation will closely approximate the *square root of the mean number of counts*. For example, suppose the following numbers of counts are obtained in successive experiments, counting for one minute each time:

1445	1468
1536	1380
1557	1541
1446	1452
1517	1520

The mean count rate is 1486. The square root of this is 39. So if the equipment is working properly—"counting statistically"—the actual number of counts obtained should depart from the mean number by less than 39 in 68% of cases, by less than 2 × 39 in 95% of cases, by less than 3 × 39 in 99·7% of cases. Let us check:

1445—1486	=	41
1536		50
1557		71
1446		40
1517		31
1468		18
1380		106
1541		55
1452		34
1520		34

In a sample of ten cases this is about what would be expected. This is a most useful way of checking equipment for intermittent behaviour.

Further Reading

ELMORE and SANDS, *Electronics*, McGraw-Hill, New York, 1949.
COOK and DUNCAN, *Modern Radiochemical Practice*, O.U.P., London, 1952.
BLEULER and GOLDSMITH, *Experimental Nucleonics*, Pitman, London, 1952.
MELOAN and KISER, *Instrumental Analysis*, Merrill, Columbus, Ohio, 1963.

PRACTICAL

1. Construct the Schmitt discriminator shown in Fig. 24.2, and observe its operation by measuring the threshold control voltage and the collector voltage of Q2. Measure the upper and lower threshold voltages, and hence calibrate the threshold control in terms of pulse height. Check your calibration by use of a pulse generator and oscilloscope.

2. If you are not already familiar with the process, carry out a series of counts of background, and of a standard radioactive source, on a Geiger or scintillation counter and scaler. Correct for background and paralysis time, and check that the equipment is counting statistically.

3. If available, a scintillation counter, decade scaler and pulse-height analyser should be examined, and the features described in this chapter observed.

CHAPTER 25

REGULATED SYSTEMS

25.1. INTRODUCTION

A regulated system is one in which departure from a desired state results in an automatic response tending to restore the state. Examples have already been discussed, in the potentiometric recorder and the regulated power supply. Systems of this type are extremely important in the field of engineering, and equally so in biology; their basic property is that they actively resist the effect of changes in their environment. A knowledge of the general principles involved is applicable to both engineering and biology. Although a detailed mathematical study of these systems can be very involved, the main features can be brought out quite simply. The temperature regulation of a heated water bath will be taken as an example; it is also a useful study in its own right.

25.2. BEHAVIOUR OF UNREGULATED WATER BATH

In Fig. 25.1 is shown a well-stirred water bath of volume V cubic centimetres, which is being heated at a rate Q calorie per second, which is losing

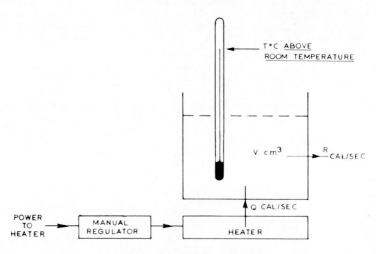

FIG. 25.1. Water bath and heater.

172

heat by radiation, conduction and convection at a rate R calorie per second, and which at time t seconds after turning on the heater is at a temperature T degrees Centigrade *above that of the room*.

Suppose that initially the bath is at room temperature, and the heat is turned off. Then $T = 0$, $Q = 0$, $R = 0$, and the bath is said to be in thermal *equilibrium* with its surroundings. At a time $t = 0$, let a constant source of heat providing Q calorie per second be applied to the bath. Since it has a volume V, by definition the bath temperature will commence to rise at a rate Q/V degree per second. As soon as it exceeds room temperature, a loss of heat will commence which will be directly proportional to the excess:

$$R = aT, \tag{25.1}$$

where a calorie per second per degree Centigrade is the *bath constant*. Thus if at some time t the bath is at a temperature $T°C$ above ambient, the net rate of gain of heat will be $(Q - R)$ calorie per second, and so the bath temperature must be rising at a rate $(Q - R)/V$ degree per second. In formal terms

$$\frac{\mathrm{d}T}{\mathrm{d}t} = \frac{Q - R}{V}, \tag{25.2}$$

but since $R = aT$,

$$\frac{\mathrm{d}T}{\mathrm{d}t} = \frac{Q - aT}{V}$$
$$= \frac{Q}{V} - \frac{aT}{V}. \tag{25.3}$$

In general terms, as the temperature rises, so will R rise, and the net rate of gain of heat $(Q - R)$ will become less and less, and so will the rate of rise of temperature. Eventually the system will reach a *steady state*, at which $R = Q$, and $\mathrm{d}T/\mathrm{d}t = 0$, at some constant temperature T_c. (It can be seen that the equilibrium condition is a special case of steady state, in which $R = Q = 0$).

The differential eqn. (25.3) may be solved for T as a function of time by any of the standard methods; the solution is

$$T = \frac{Q}{a}(1 - \varepsilon^{-at/V}). \tag{25.4}$$

This gives an exponentially rising curve of a form identical with that of the voltage of a condenser charging through a resistance, as shown in Fig. 25.2. It will be seen from eqn. (25.4) that

$$T_c = \frac{Q}{a} \tag{25.5}$$

and that the curve has a time constant

$$\tau = \frac{V}{a}. \tag{25.6}$$

This curve is the inverse of Newton's cooling curve. The bath is characterised by its bath constant; the time constant then follows.

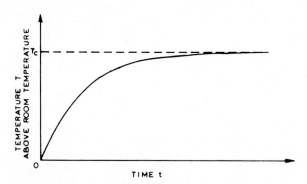

FIG. 25.2. Heating curve for water bath.

From a knowledge of the bath constant, the required heating power for any steady-state temperature above ambient can be determined:

$$W = Ja \quad W/°C, \tag{25.7}$$

where J is Joule's constant, 4·18 joule/cal. The constant a for a given bath is best determined by filling the bath with warm water, and observing the rate of cooling in degrees per second for a given temperature T above ambient. Then, since $Q = 0$,

$$\frac{dT}{dt} = -\frac{aT}{V} \tag{25.8}$$

in which a is the only unknown.

By doing this operation before a heater is selected, much subsequent waste of time may be avoided.

For a bath in which $Q = 10$ cal/sec, $V = 500$ cm³ and $a = 1$ cal/sec/°C,

$$T_c = \frac{Q}{a} = 10°C \text{ above ambient}$$

$$\tau = \frac{V}{a} = 500 \text{ sec.}$$

and the initial rate of rise $= Q/V = 0·05$ degree/sec.

The bath will take four time constants, about half an hour, to come within 1% of its final temperature.

25.3. REGULATED WATER BATH: ON–OFF CONTROL

If the manual regulator in the last section is replaced by a relay, which is operated by a pair of contacts sealed into the stem of the thermometer, a regulated system results, as shown in Fig. 25.3.

If now the bath is initially at room temperature and is turned on at a time $t = 0$, the thermometer contacts are open, the relay contacts are closed, and the bath receives the maximum value of Q of which the heater is capable.

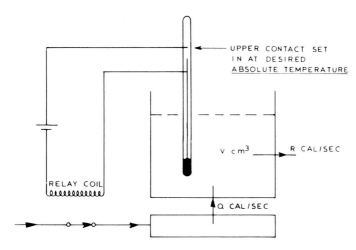

FIG. 25.3. Regulated water bath.

Following the argument of the previous section, it will be seen that the time constant V/a is unchanged, but that now $T_c\ (=Q/a)$ will be at a temperature far above that required, and that the initial rate of rise $(=Q/V)$ is much greater. For the previous example, but taking Q_{max} as 50 cal/sec,

$$T_c = 50°C \text{ above ambient}$$

$$\frac{Q}{V} = 0.25 \text{ degree/sec.}$$

The temperature–time curve will follow this path until the thermometer contacts close, and open the relay contacts, when the curve will flatten off. Owing to the thermal capacity of the heater unit, the bath will rise a little above the temperature set by the upper thermometer contact. It will then start out on an exponential cooling curve towards room temperature. This will continue only until the thermometer contacts open again, and heating is resumed; the cycle of closing and opening will then repeat indefinitely. The bath temperature will fluctuate up and down by a fraction of a degree (the differential), but this can be made as small as desired by suitable design. Further, this temperature is now *absolute*, and independent of room temperature or fluctuations in the heater supply.

Figure 25.4 shows the behaviour of the bath in the numerical example, with and without regulation.

To make the differential small, the value of T_c must not exceed the desired bath temperature greatly. This, however, makes initial heating from room temperature slow, and it is usual to provide a booster heater for the initial heating. This is cut out manually when the operating temperature is reached.

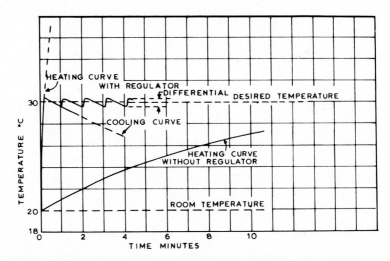

Fig. 25.4. Behaviour of water bath.

25.4. PROPORTIONAL CONTROL

If the thermometer contacts and relay of the previous section were replaced by a heater regulator arranged to vary Q *in proportion to the error* between the actual and desired bath temperatures, a much smoother control could be achieved. In the case of a water bath this is not necessary, but there are many cases where proportional control is desirable and is used. The electronically regulated power supply is an example; the potentiometric recorder is another, except that the system overloads for large errors, and is truly proportional only when close to its desired position. Many physiological examples of proportional control are available.

Practical systems which embody proportional control require careful design if their operation is to be stable. In mathematical terms, the equation for the system is a differential one of second or higher order, and the solution to such an equation may take one of three forms, depending on the physical constants of the system. The system may be *overdamped, critically damped* or *underdamped*. For a temperature regulator the behaviour after switching on will follow one of the patterns of Fig. 25.5, depending on the various thermal time constants in the system.

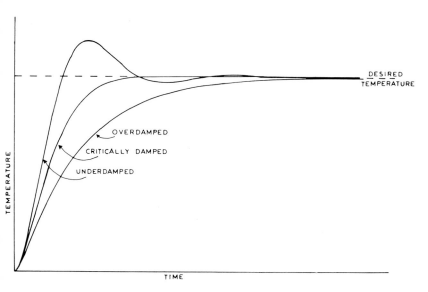

FIG. 25.5. Response of a water bath using proportional control.

The critically damped curve is the one to be desired, since it gives the fastest possible rise without overshoot. Provision is usually made to adjust the damping of proportionally controlled systems; a typical method will be discussed in Chapter 27 for a potentiometric recorder.

25.5. REGULATED SYSTEMS IN GENERAL

The type of regulated system described above may be represented by a block diagram, as in Fig. 25.6.

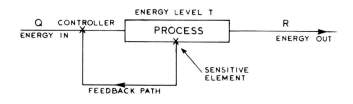

FIG. 25.6. Regulation by control of input.

A second type of regulated system is as shown in Fig. 25.7.

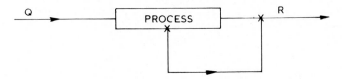

Fig. 25.7. Regulation by control of output.

It will be seen that this type is less economical of energy than the first, since Q is permanently at its maximum value, and T is controlled by wasting a greater or lesser amount of energy by way of R. It may have certain practical advantages, especially since it hastens a *fall* in T. A combination of both types is not uncommon.

Further Reading

TERMAN, *Electronic and Radio Engineering* (4th ed.), McGraw-Hill, New York, 1955.
HAMMOND, *Feedback Theory*, English Universities Press, London, 1958.
ASHBY, *An Introduction to Cybernetics*, Methuen, London, 1956.

PRACTICAL

1.   Determine the bath constant of a large beaker of water, using the method described in this chapter, and hence derive its time constant. Keep it well stirred. What electrical heating power would be required to maintain it at 37°C in a room at 25°C, and at 10°C? Light a low burner under it, and plot the initial rate of rise of temperature. What value of Q have you set in? What final steady-state temperature would the bath reach, and about how long would it take?

2.   Sketch a block diagram of the system involved when you move your finger to touch a spot of ink on the surface of a table. How could this system become oscillatory?

3.   Regulated systems often embody a human operator as part of the feedback loop, and some mechanical device as the remainder. Sketch the system involved in manipulating a hot shower for satisfactory results. How can this system become oscillatory, and how is it normally stabilised?

4.   If available set up a water bath with electrical heater, thermostat and stirrer, and record its temperature by means of a resistance thermometer, pseudo-Wheatstone bridge and potentiometric recorder. (The thermometer and Wheatstone bridge can easily be improvised.) How good is the thermostat? What is the effect of excessive heating power?

5.   Design features of any other available regulated system should be examined, and the accuracy of control observed.

CHAPTER 26

TRANSDUCERS

TRANSDUCERS are devices for the conversion of one variable into another; as generally encountered, the term is used specifically for those intended to convert other variables, usually mechanical ones, into electrical form for subsequent amplification, transmission, display or storage. Table 26.1 summarises the types most commonly used.

26.1. DISPLACEMENT TRANSDUCERS

(a) Potentiometers

These are available with fairly frictionless bearings and wipers, in both rotating and linear forms. The resolution of displacement is limited to the distance between turns of the wire used. Although high quality transducer potentiometers are fairly expensive, in many cases they save so much associated circuitry that they are always worth considering. They may be supplied with either DC or AC of a frequency to suit the associated equipment. AC amplification is far easier to arrange than DC, but it is much harder to provide the potentiometer with a source of constant amplitude AC.

(b) Linear variable differential transformer (LVDT)

This consists of three windings, connected as shown in Fig. 26.1.

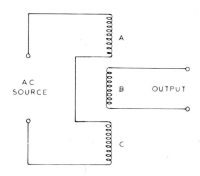

FIG. 26.1. Linear variable differential transformer.

179

Windings A and C are connected in opposition, so that no net output is induced in B. If now an iron core is inserted, this balance will be preserved if it is situated symmetrically: but if it is displaced up or down it unbalances the system, and an output appears at B. The phase of this output will be reversed as the core goes through the null position, so the direction of movement can be determined after amplification by *phase-sensitive detection*. This is fully discussed by Donaldson, and by Volume 19 of the MIT Radiation Laboratory Series. Unfortunately there is not a complete absence of signal at the null position, harmonics of the source frequency still being present.

Methods of minimising this effect are available; alternatively, the transducer can be operated always on one side of the balance position. These transformers are quite readily constructed for any particular application, and are also available commercially in many different forms.

(c) *Variable inductor or condenser*

These are simple to construct in a variety of forms; the variable condenser is particularly suited for measuring the movement of a diaphragm with pressure changes. By moving an iron or iron-dust core partially inserted into an inductor a fairly linear change in inductance with displacement can be produced over a considerable range. A linear change in capacitance with rotation is available in many small variable condensers manufactured for short-wave radio tuning; types intended for automatic tuning and incorporating ball races are very suitable. As was discussed in §6.2, the capacitance of a parallel plate condenser is given by

$$C(\text{pF}) = \frac{0 \cdot 0884 ANK}{d},$$

where A is the area of one plate in square centimetres, N is the number of *dielectrics* in a multi-plate condenser, K is the dielectric constant ($= 1$ in air) and d is the spacing between plates in centimetres.

If two plates only are used, and their separation is varied by the displacement, it will be seen that capacitance varies *inversely* with displacement. However, the relation is sufficiently linear for displacements which are small compared with the spacing between the plates.

To convert change of capacitance or inductance to a voltage output, it may be used to detune a crystal oscillator tank circuit, to detune a tuned-grid tuned-plate oscillator circuit, or to detune a tank circuit followed by a phase-sensitive detector. These methods are all discussed by Donaldson, by Dickinson and by Hansen, in the references given at the end of this chapter. The changes may also be used to vary an oscillator or multivibrator frequency: this frequency can be counted digitally or indicated on a suitable frequency meter.

(d) *Photoelectric*

For the range of displacements from 100 μ to 1 cm, and accuracies of 1%
or less, the displacement may be used to vary the amount of light passing
from a constant source of illumination to a photocell. Since different regions
of photocathode have different sensitivities, it is important to maintain a
constant area under illumination, which varies in intensity: this can be done
by the use of collimating and focusing lenses, and placing the variable
aperture in the parallel light beam between them, as shown in Fig. 26.2.

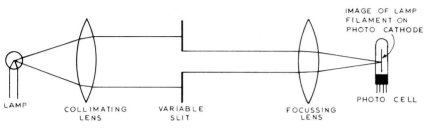

FIG. 26.2. Optical transducer.

The lamp filament must be maintained accurately at constant current, since
illumination varies as the fourth power of current: this may be done by use
of a transistor series regulator. If it is desired to use AC amplification after
the photocell the light beam may be chopped mechanically by a revolving
sector disc, or a gas discharge lamp fed from a multivibrator may be used.
For more accurate or finer measurements, there are two excellent digital
methods. For the range 10 μ up, moiré fringes may be used. Two transparent
slides with alternate clear and opaque bands are prepared, one with, say, 10
bands/cm, the other with 11. If these are set up in a beam of light, they will
behave like a scale and its vernier. For each movement of 1 mm of the moving
graticule, a dark shadow will move from one end of the graticules to the other,
and these may be counted by a photocell and displayed on a digital counter.
The second method, for very fine movements, uses monochromatic light,
and the interference fringes produced as the angle of a very thin wedge of air
between two optically flat glass plates is varied. The fringes again are counted
with a photocell.

26.2. VELOCITY TRANSDUCERS

(a) *Moving coil*

If a conductor of length *d* cm is caused to move across a magnetic field of strength H lines per cm² at a velocity of v cm/sec, an EMF E V will appear across its ends, given by

$$E = 10^{-8}vdH. \qquad (26.1)$$

Since a field strength of about 2000 lines/cm² is about the maximum available in practice, it will be seen that a conductor 1 cm long will produce an EMF of 20 μV per centimetre per second of velocity. A great many types of velocity transducer are based on this principle.

(b) Electromagnetic flowmeter

The principle set out above may also be used for measurement of fluid flow velocity. Provided that the fluid is a conductor, it will generate an EMF proportional to its velocity if placed in a magnetic field. However, a steady EMF of the small magnitude occurring in practice is very difficult to distinguish from small polarisation potentials inevitable with the use of reversible electrodes in contact with the fluid. The use of an alternating field will produce an alternating potential at the same frequency, and proportional to the velocity, but also it generates another alternating component independent of the velocity in the associated connecting leads. Fortunately, this is in a phase at 90° to the velocity component, so they can be separated by phase-sensitive detection. An alternative approach is to use a square-wave magnetic field, which is the equivalent to a DC, reversed often enough to overcome polarisation effects. This also produces spurious potentials every time it reverses, but by suitable switching these potentials can be eliminated at the amplifier output. The state of development of these instruments can be seen from the PGBME Symposium cited in the references; they can be used with fixed probes in a cannula inserted in the blood vessel, or with lower accuracy the probes can be applied directly to the walls of the vessel without opening it. It is quite practicable to leave the whole transducer head chronically implanted about a blood vessel in an experimental animal.

(c) Ultrasonic flowmeters

These depend on the apparent change in velocity of a sound wave propagated alternately with and against a moving stream of fluid. Basically the method is excellent, but in practice many difficulties are encountered. These also are described in the PGBME Symposium listed in the references.

(d) Resistance flowmeters

These are chiefly used to measure gas flow velocities. In general, an obstruction such as a metal plate with an orifice in it placed in a tube carrying a flow of fluid will give a pressure drop across it which is proportional to the square of the flow velocity. However, if the obstruction consists of a very fine wire mesh (typically 300–400 wires to the inch) the pressure drop is small, but directly proportional to the flow velocity over a wide range of velocities. The pressure difference produced in this way may be used to displace a diaphragm, whose movement is then detected by use of a capacitance transducer or linear variable differential transformer. An alternative linear resistance, due to Fleisch, consists of a cluster of parallel small tubes placed as an obstruction in the tube carrying the fluid flow.

(e) *Thermal flowmeters*

The flow velocity of a liquid can be measured by adding heat at a point in the stream, and measuring either the steady-state increase in heat downstream or the time of transit over a known distance of a pulse of heat. The flow velocity of either a liquid or a gas can be measured by estimating the cooling effect on a heated element inserted in the stream; this is usually done by making the heated element of some material of high temperature coefficient of resistance, and connecting it as one arm of a Wheatstone bridge. A second arm of the same material may be used to compensate for changes in ambient temperature of the stream. Suitable materials are nickel or platinum, or, alternatively, a thermistor can be used. In cases where explosive gas mixtures are in use, as in anaesthesia, the temperature of the heated element can be as little as 0·5°C above ambient, and no danger whatever of ignition exists. For very rapid fluctuations in flow rate, either a very fine unmounted thermistor (diameter 50 μ) can be used, or a filament of Wollaston wire. This consists of a fine platinum wire coated with ten times its thickness of silver. The wire is mounted in the required position, and the silver layer is then etched off the central part electrolytically, using a drop of dilute nitric acid suspended from a platinum loop.

26.3. FORCE OR PRESSURE

(a) *Resistance strain gauge*

If a wire is subjected to tension, it both increases in length and decreases in diameter; provided that the tension is within the elastic limits of the wire, it will return to its original shape when the tension is removed. Both the increase in length and the decrease in diameter contribute to an increase in resistance, which is quite accurately proportional to the tension applied. If the strain in the wire is defined as extension per unit length, $\delta l/l$, then the increase in resistance per unit resistance, $\delta R/R$, is related to the strain by a constant factor for each material; this constant is generally about 2. The maximum change in resistance that can be produced without exceeding the elastic limits of a wire is usually about 1%; by connecting the wire as one arm of a Wheatstone bridge, the tension can be measured. To increase the output from the bridge, and to compensate for ambient temperature changes, it is usual to use all four arms of the bridge as tension-detecting elements. One common arrangement is shown diagrammatically in Fig. 26.3. The four wires *A*, *B*, *C* and *D* are mounted in a rigid insulating frame, and are pre-stressed. The tension to be measured is applied to a cross bar linking their centres, and they are connected to form a Wheatstone bridge, as shown :

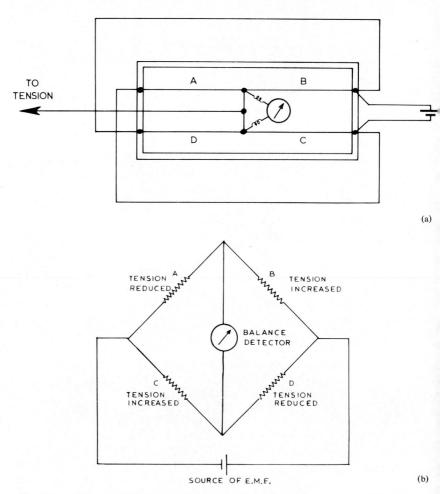

FIG. 26.3. Unbonded resistance strain gauge. (a) Mechanical arrangement. (b) Circuit.

When tension is applied, it adds to the initial tension in *B* and *C*, and sub-tracts from it in *A* and *D*, thus producing maximum unbalance in the bridge. If carefully manufactured, resistance strain gauges give very accurate and reproducible results. They may be used in the *unbonded form* shown above or in the *bonded form*. Bonded gauges consist of fine wires on a thin paper backing, which are rigidly cemented to the surface whose extension is to be measured. Again four gauges are normally used, in a Wheatstone bridge; two are placed to measure the extension, and two to provide temperature compensation. Most bonded gauges have a gauge factor of about 2, but recently semiconductor gauges with a factor of over a hundred have become available. At present they are much more expensive than standard gauges.

For direct blood pressure measurements, the pressure is used to produce minute displacements of a fairly rigid diaphragm; these displacements may then be measured by capacitance transducer, linear variable differential transformer or unbonded strain gauge. (In this field the unbonded strain gauge transducers produced by Statham are in very wide use; they show negligible drift in zero or sensitivity, and once calibrated may be relied on for long periods.) The response to rapid pressure changes by a transducer is much reduced if a long catheter or thin needle is used in conjunction with it; the monograph by Hansen cited in the references at the end of this chapter should be consulted in this regard.

(b) *Piezoelectric strain gauge*

These devices depend on the fact that many crystals show the property of piezoelectricity; if stressed along a suitable axis, electric charges appear between opposite faces. Materials normally used are quartz, Rochelle salt or tourmaline, or synthetics, such as barium titanate. If the stress is maintained the charges produced tend to leak away, both through or around the crystal, and through the external measuring circuit; but for rapidly alternating stresses this is unimportant. Many gramophone pickups are of this type, and can form the basis of transducers for biological measurements.

(c) *Vacuum-tube strain gauge*

The RCA type 5734 is a subminiature triode, in which the plate structure can be moved with relation to the grid, through a diaphragm. The principle of the gauge is shown in Fig. 26.4.

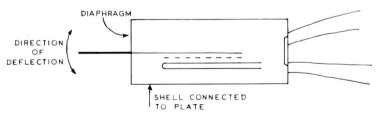

FIG. 26.4. Triode strain gauge.

The maximum angle of deflection of the plate pin is ± 0.5 degree, and a greater amount will permanently damage the tube. The metal shell of the tube is connected to the plate; it must be clamped in a metal heat sink in use, but is very sensitive to mechanical distortion. In a new tube an output of ± 40 V can be expected for a deflection of $\pm 0.5°$, but this appears to diminish quite rapidly with use, and fairly frequent recalibration is necessary. The plate pin may be extended by cementing an additional length of rigid wire to it if required; some form of limitation of its travel is essential if damage is to be prevented.

TABLE 26.1.

TRANSDUCERS

Type of Transducer	Range of Variable	Output	Notes
	(1) Displacement		
Potentiometer	25 μ up	DC or AC	Simple, produces large highly stable output, but frictional effects always present.
Variable differential transformer	1 μ −10 cm	AC	May be made very small. Linear over the full range of displacement, except for slight spurious output near zero. Output voltage small but highly stable.
Variable inductor or capacitor	1 μ −1 mm	AC	May be made small, simple to make. Linear only over a small range of displacement, rather complex circuitry required. Small output, rather unstable.
Photoelectric	100 Å up	DC or AC	Rather bulky. May have digital output for use with scaler. Highly linear. Large output, highly stable.
	(2) Velocity (a) Mechanical		
Moving coil	Any	DC	Depends on Faraday's law. Accuracy governed by uniformity of magnetic field used.
	(b) Fluid		
Electromagnetic	1 cm/sec up	DC or AC	Depends on Faraday's law. May be used on unopened blood vessels. Requires a conducting fluid. Complex circuitry required for stability.
Ultrasonic	1 cm/sec up	AC	Complex, requires further development. May be used on unopened blood vessels. Rather bulky.
Resistance	1 cm/sec up	—	Depends on conversion of velocity to force. Requires insertion of transducer head into fluid. Gas or liquid.
Thermal	1 mm/sec up	DC	Depends on cooling of element by fluid flow. Requires insertion of transducer head into fluid. Responds to very rapid fluctuations in velocity. Gas or liquid.

	(3) Force or Pressure		
Resistance strain gauge	1 gmwt up	AC or DC	Highly accurate; zero and calibration stable over long periods. Small output, low impedance.
Piezoelectric	1 gmwt up	AC	Fairly accurate, calibration stable over long periods. Large output, high impedance. Output is charge rather than voltage; leakage through amplifier input or across crystal surface renders system insensitive to slow changes, but excellent for vibration measurements.
Vacuum tube (RCA type 5734)	1 mgmwt up	AC or DC	Highly sensitive, but fragile and liable to drift of zero and change in calibration. Large output; suitable for either slow changes or vibration measurements up to 12 kc/s.

It should be noted that any of the displacement transducers listed above can be used as force transducers in conjunction with a spring of suitable compliance. Any of the force transducers listed can be used as displacement transducers if their inherent stiffness is negligible in the circumstances of use. Further, any force transducer can be used as an acceleration transducer in conjunction with a mass: acceleration = force/mass.

Further Reading

DONALDSON, *Electronic Apparatus for Biological Research*, Butterworth, London, 1958.
HANSEN, *Pressure Measurement in the Human Organism*, Teknisk Forlag, Copenhagen, 1949.
Professional Group for Biomedical Electronics, Institution of Radio Engineers (U.S.A.), Blood Flowmeters Symposium, 1959.
MIT Radiation Laboratory Series, vol. 19, *Waveforms*, McGraw-Hill, New York, 1949.
DICKINSON, *Electrophysiological Technique*, Electronic Engineering, London, 1950.
YARNELL, *Resistance Strain Gauges*, Electronic Engineering, London, 1951.
OSTER and NISHIJIMA, Moiré Patterns, *Scientific American*, May, 1963.

PRACTICAL

1. Construct a large linear variable differential transformer, as described in this chapter. Supply the input from a filament transformer connected to the AC supply line, and use an oscilloscope to observe the output as a piece of soft iron is moved through the null position.

2. Construct a pair of moiré graticules by ruling thick India ink lines at regular close intervals across two strips of tracing paper, as described in this chapter. Place one behind the other, hold them up to the light, and move one with respect to the other.

3. Observe the operation of any other type of transducer which may be available.

CHAPTER 27

TRANSMISSION AND STORAGE OF DATA

27.1. BASIS OF COMMUNICATION THEORY

For any serious consideration of the rate of transmission of information from one point to another, a quantitative method of estimating "amount of information" must be set up. This is done on the following basis. Suppose that a man is waiting for a bus, and an official informs him "There will be a bus here within the next hour". This evidently conveys little information to him—he already knows that this is very probable. But if he is told "There will be no bus here within the next hour", this conveys a great deal of information. In fact it alters the *probability* of the arrival of a bus by a large amount, *as far as the prospective traveller is concerned*. If the information is conveyed by a bystander instead of an official, the information content is probably less.

The mathematical definition of information usually adopted involves the logarithms of probabilities. If an event occurs and a message is transmitted telling about the occurrence, the amount of information transmitted is defined as

$$\log_2 \left[\frac{\text{probability of the event to the receiver after the message is received}}{\text{probability of the event to the receiver before the message is received}} \right] \tag{27.1}$$

The unit of information is called the "bit". The special case in which the receiver is certain that the message received is correct is called the "noiseless" case. In this case the probability of the event to the receiver after the message is received is unity, and the expression becomes:

$$\text{Information received} = -\log_2 \left[\begin{array}{c} \text{probability of the event to the} \\ \text{receiver before the message is} \\ \text{received} \end{array} \right] \tag{27.2}$$

As an example, if a baby is born, the information "It's a boy" decides the question as to one of two probabilities. If these are assumed to have been equally likely, the probability before the message was received was $\frac{1}{2}$, so

$$\text{quantity of information} = -\log_2(\tfrac{1}{2})$$
$$= \log_2(2) = 1,$$

188

i.e. one *bit* of information tells which of two equally likely possibilities has been chosen. By this means the rate of transmission of information can be expressed in terms of bits per unit time.

Now for any given channel of transmission of information, it can be shown that a maximum rate of transmission exists, and this can be calculated in specific cases. If information is supplied at a higher rate, either part will be lost, or part must be stored until the rate of supply drops.

This upper limit of rate of transmission applies also to the rate at which data can be assimilated by a human observer, either visually or aurally. This limitation can be seen, for example, in the inability of even a trained observer to absorb all the information available from electrocardiographic recording from a patient as it is made, in real time. A complete representation would show the fluctuating potentials all over the body surface from instant to instant as a function of time. A sufficient representation can be obtained by sampling the potentials from three suitable points on the surface and displaying them separately as functions of time; but no human observer can assimilate this information at the rate at which it is being produced. By making a permanent recording, the rate of presentation of data can be slowed down suitably; alternatively, the data can be examined in real time one channel at a time, or a "vectorcardiogram" can be displayed, in which one potential is displayed as a function of a second one, and the time dependence of each is minimised. This limitation of the human operator is a vital factor in human engineering, the study of adapting machines to suit the operator's capabilities.

For these reasons, methods of data presentation and storage have received a great deal of attention.

27.2. FREQUENCY RESPONSE

The greater the rate of transmission of information required in a channel of information, the wider must be the range of frequencies it can pass, since information can only be transmitted by a varying signal. Thus a half-tone picture can be transmitted in a minute over a telephone line with a bandwidth of 3 kc/s, or in a twentieth of a second over a television channel with a bandwidth of 3 mc/s.

27.3. SYSTEMS FOR DATA STORAGE

Table 27.1 at the end of this chapter summarises the various methods available for data storage. They are discussed in more detail in the following section.

(a) *Potentiometric recorders*

Potentiometric recorders have already been discussed in principle in Chapter 4. They are of high accuracy, but are relatively slow in response, so are limited in use to slowly changing variables. A typical recorder would require 1 or 2 sec to traverse the full chart width. Sensitivity is high, usually in the range 0·5–100 mV for full-scale deflection, but most recorders can be used only with low-resistance sources, typically less than 1000 ohm. (High input impedance recorders are obtainable, but are not common.) Chart widths of 6 in. and 10 in. are normal, and recorders are available for simultaneous recording of two variables. Sampling recorders, printing out distinctive dots for six or more variables in rotation, are also in common use. A further variant is the *X–Y* recorder, in which two potentiometer movements drive the pen along axes at right angles to each other, and so allow the automatic plotting of functions of a variable other than time.

The block diagram of Fig. 27.1 is typical for a simple recorder.

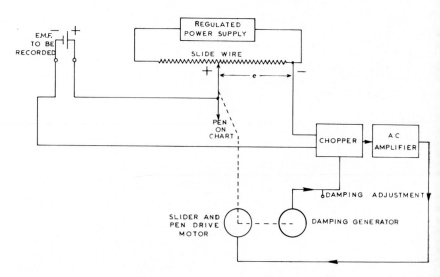

FIG. 27.1. Potentiometric recorder.

The slide wire is fed from a regulated power supply, and the voltage *e* picked off from it is connected in opposition to the EMF to be recorded. The difference is converted into AC by a mechanical chopper, amplified and used to drive an AC motor which moves the slider and pen. On the same shaft as the AC motor is a small damping generator, whose output is proportional to the motor *speed*. This is connected in such a way that it provides a braking force proportional to motor speed; "the faster it goes, the more it can't." When correctly adjusted, the pen will move rapidly up to the correct reading when an EMF is applied, and then stop, as shown in Fig. 27.2.

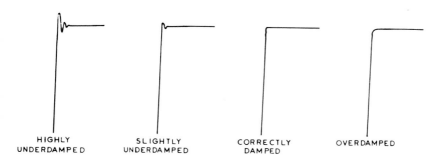

| HIGHLY UNDERDAMPED | SLIGHTLY UNDERDAMPED | CORRECTLY DAMPED | OVERDAMPED |

Fig. 27.2. Damping adjustment of potentiometric recorder.

The standardising circuit, by which the instrument can be calibrated from a standard cell, is not shown.

(b) *Pen recorders*

Pen recorders are widely used for storage and display of biological information, and in their modern form are very reliable, sensitive and accurate. They can readily be given a frequency response up to 100 c/s or better. Various types of suspension are in use, most being modifications of the moving-coil meter movement, or of a loudspeaker movement. Pens writing with ink are probably the most satisfactory for general use, but they splatter ink if violently overdriven. Moreover, nearly all write on a curvilinear chart shaped to suit the pen radius, which can be difficult to read. Various forms of heat sensitive paper are available, and using a hot stylus a rectilinear recording can be obtained; these are not very satisfactory at fast writing speeds, however, and the paper is expensive. A special conducting paper, Teledeltos, has been used extensively in the past in conjunction with a current-carrying stylus, but this does not produce as clear a record as the other two types.

Modern recorders are invariably transistorised, and are driven either by a pair of power emitter followers, or by one of the more elaborate bridge circuits used in high-fidelity audio amplifiers for loudspeaker operation. Some provision for adjustment of damping is important; for reliable operation the pen-to-paper friction should represent a negligible part of the damping provided.

(c) *Photographic recording*

Photographic recording has been widely used in the past, but in its original form has the disadvantage that processing is required before the record can be inspected. For frequencies above about 1 kc/s, the combination of a camera and oscilloscope is still the best method available. For a continuous record of non-recurrent phenomena, such as an EMG, no time base is used on the oscilloscope, and a strip of film is moved through the camera at constant speed to generate a time base. For recurrent phenomena, or short samples of nonrecurrent phenomena, the oscilloscope screen is simply photographed. This may be done with ordinary film, or by use of the Polaroid–Land process if immediate results are more important than cost of operation.

For multi-channel recording of phenomena in the range 0 to about 5 kc/s a bank of mirror galvanometers can be used, in conjunction with film moving at constant speed. Special sensitised papers used with an ultraviolet light source have made it possible to obtain a record without processing the film, but the system has a number of disadvantages for general biological use. It is widely used in the engineering field.

(d) *Magnetic-tape recording*

For temporary data storage in the biological range, a suitable tape re-corder is most useful. In particular it permits editing of material before a permanent record is made, so that a considerable waste of recording paper or film is avoided. The tapes can be re-used almost indefinitely, and a spoken commentary can be added to the record. One, two and four track recorders are readily available, and more tracks can be obtained if required.

However, commercial recorders intended for reproduction of voice or music can be used only over a very limited range of frequencies; most biological data contain frequencies too low for their capabilities. By the use of a frequency or pulse-modulation system, however, the whole biological range can be spanned. Such recorders are manufactured both in the United States and Britain, but are quite expensive.

(e) *Storage oscilloscopes*

A number of manufacturers of oscilloscopes produce one or more models incorporating a method of storing the image produced by a single sweep across the screen. Although these instruments are rather expensive, they have great value in biological and medical investigation, since a transient phenom-enon such as an electromyogram can be examined in detail immediately after its occurrence, and photographed if it is desired to retain it permanently. The definition of traces stored in this way is not as good as that of normal oscilloscope traces, but is quite adequate for most purposes.

(f) *Digital storage*

A highly effective but expensive method of data storage is that of conversion to digital form, and retention of the digits in a magnetic core memory, such as is used in digital computers. The incoming signal, which is varying with time, is said to be in *analogue* form; analogue to digital conversion involves the sampling of the magnitude of the analogue signal at sufficiently frequent intervals to represent all its significant changes adequately, and then converting each magnitude into a number. These numbers are stored in binary form by magnetising very small rings of ferrite material in one direction or the other. To store 400 numbers, each in the range of 0–511, in this form would require 4000 of these ferrite rings, with their associated circuitry. Stored information is retained indefinitely, even if the apparatus is switched off, until deliberately erased. It can be read out of the system repetitively in analogue form, sufficiently rapidly to give an apparently stationary pattern on an oscilloscope, or sufficiently slowly to allow it to be plotted by a potentiometric recorder; it can be printed out on tape or by typewriter as a set of numbers, or punched on tape or cards for subsequent computation on a digital computer.

27.4. DATA AVERAGING

If an experiment is repeated a number of times, the response will, in general, contain a number of *regular* features, which are related to the experimenter's manipulations, and a number of *random* features, which are not. By taking the sum, point by point, of the responses to a series of experiments, the regular features are caused to add linearly; the random features add in proportion to $\sqrt{n}$, where n is the number of experiments. The net result is a gain in *signal to noise ratio* of $n/\sqrt{n}$, or $\sqrt{n}$, by adding n experiments. In practice the background "noise" is never truly random, and the improvement in signal to noise ratio is not as good as $\sqrt{n}$, but is certainly considerable.

This summing process can be carried out very simply in conjunction with digital storage, since the addition of successive experiments may be done as the experiments proceed. A monitoring oscilloscope is used to show the contents of the digital store, and experiments can be stopped as soon as the signal to noise ratio is adequate. In this way minute signals can be extracted from noise which obscures them completely in any one experiment.

14

TABLE 27.1.

METHODS OF DATA STORAGE

Type of Storage System	Frequency Response	Remarks
(1) Visual Data Retrieval Potentiometric recorder	0–1 c/s	High precision; 1–0·1% accuracy.
Meter or loudspeaker movement driving stylus (a) ink (b) Teledeltos (c) heat	0–1000 c/s	Response is dependent on construction of individual unit, and generally requires careful adjustment for critical damping. Typical response is 0–100 c/s, but 0–1000 c/s can be obtained by use of ink-jet recording.
Photographic (a) mirror galvanometer	0–5 kc/s	Recording by visible or UV light is possible. The record obtained is rather unsatisfactory.
(b) from oscilloscope screen	0–100 mc/s or more	Accurate to about 2% at best. May use either single frame photography of a stationary oscilloscope trace, or moving film for a continuous record of a nonrecurrent phenomenon.
(2) Electrical Data Retrieval Magnetic tape recording (a) amplitude modulation	50 c/s–1 kc/s	Considerable phase distortion of low-frequency components.
(b) pulse modulation	0–20 kc/s	Very good, but fairly expensive.
Digital memory	0–10 kc/s	Very good, but expensive. Permits data summing to improve signal to noise ratio.

Further Reading

GOLDMAN, *Information Theory*, Prentice-Hall, New York, 1953.

MIT Radiation Laboratory Series, vol. 22, *Cathode Ray Tube Displays*, McGraw-Hill, New York, 1949.

KNOLL and KAZAN, *Storage Tubes*, Wiley, New York, 1952.

RENWICK, *Digital Storage Systems*, Spon, London, 1964.

PRACTICAL

1. Using a biological preamplifier as constructed in Chapter 22, obtain an ECG on your oscilloscope from lead I (right arm to left arm). Set up a second preamplifier to obtain the ECG from lead II (right arm to left leg). Now apply the lead II output to the X driver amplifier of the oscilloscope, in place of its own time base. (Disconnect the grid of the bootstrap cathode follower (V5 pin 7), from the time base circuit, and connect it temporarily to the moving arm of a 1 M potentiometer. Earth the bottom of the potentiometer, and take the top of it to the lead II preamplifier output.) The result will be the Lissajous figure produced by the two ECGs, which in this case approximates a vectocardiogram. (A true

vectocardiogram is obtained by applying pairs of body leads taken at right angles to each other.) Observe the effect of deep inspiration and expiration on the direction of the major loop, which is produced by the QRS complex of the ECG.

2. Other experiments will depend largely on available recording equipment. Typical good experiments are the adjustment of damping on a potentiometric recorder, the measurement of frequency response and accuracy of a pen or heat writing recorder, and the fidelity of a tape recorder using square-wave recording.

CHAPTER 28

SOME BIOLOGICAL ANALYTICAL METHODS

28.1. SODIUM, POTASSIUM, CALCIUM IONS

These ions, which are the least amenable to direct chemical analysis, are routinely estimated by the flame spectrophotometer. This consists of a gas flame, normally colourless, into which may be introduced at a constant rate a fine spray of the solution to be analysed. Atoms of solute are excited at the high temperature, outer-shell electrons moving out into orbits of higher energy. Whenever one of these atoms reverts to a lower energy level, light of a characteristic wavelength is emitted. This light enters the spectrometer by a narrow slit, and is then broken into its characteristic spectrum, usually by means of a diffraction grating. As the grating is slowly rotated by means of a calibrated wavelength dial, light of the narrow band of wavelengths selected is caused to fall on an outlet slit, behind which is a photomultiplier tube. The resulting current flows through a very high resistance, producing a voltage drop, and this in turn is measured by a standard potentiometric method. Balance is indicated by an amplifier and meter. By calibrating the instrument in terms of voltage drop against concentration, using known solutions, it becomes possible to estimate unknown concentrations.

If an instrument is required specifically for the estimation of sodium, potassium or calcium ions, a considerable simplification can be made at the expense of some accuracy. The wavelength analyser section of the apparatus is replaced by simple optical filters, one for each ion to be estimated, and a much less sensitive photocell system is used, connected directly to a micro-ammeter. Instruments of this type are very common for routine clinical investigation of biological fluids. The book by Kay (see the references at the end of this chapter) should be consulted for a comprehensive review of these techniques.

28.2. CHLORIDE ION

Chloride analyses are usually performed by titration with silver ion, using an electrometric end-point indication. Cotlove's method is based on the fact that a silver electrode is reversible only in a solution of silver ions. Accordingly if two silver electrodes are polarised by the application of a potential of about 0·25 V between them, as in Fig. 28.1, a significant current will flow in the circuit only if free silver ions are present in the solution. This in turn will occur only after the end point of the titration has been reached. In practice it is necessary to add a "supporting electrolyte", usually nitric acid, to the

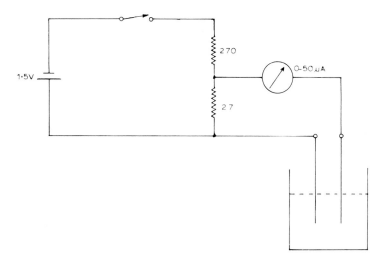

FIG. 28.1. Chloride titration end point indication.

system so that the total solution resistance is small, and a very little chloride-free protein (usually gelatin) to prevent reduction of the precipitate. The presence of additional protein will introduce a slight error, since sulphydryl groups present will also precipitate silver ion; this error is, however, negligible in estimating chloride in plasma or tissue extracts.

Silver ion can be added to the solution in the conventional fashion by means of a burette. However, for determining very small quantities of chloride this is clumsy, and Cotlove's method consists of adding silver ion electrolytically by inserting two more silver electrodes into the solution, and passing a constant current between them. The time for which the current is passed before the end point is reached is then directly related to the amount of chloride present. The original reference at the end of this chapter should be consulted for further details.

28.3. ESTIMATION OF OXYGEN AND CARBON DIOXIDE IN SOLUTION

The estimation of oxygen tension in solution is basically simple, depending on its anodic reduction at a bright platinum electrode polarised to $+0.7$ V with respect to a standard half cell. However, a number of difficulties arise in practice. Firstly, such an electrode is very readily poisoned by the adsorption of any protein present on to its surface; this can be overcome by enclosing it in a film of collodion or other suitable semi-permeable membrane. Secondly, as in all polarographic methods, the current flowing to the electrode depends on the rate of reduction of oxygen; for this to be constant and proportional to the oxygen tension, a steady and reproducible state of diffusion of oxygen through the adjoining layers of solution towards the electrode must be established. This in turn implies either an unstirred solution or a constant flow rate past the electrode, and a constant viscosity and temperature of the solution. There have been a great many ingenious methods of meeting these requirements; typical modern techniques are described in the references cited. In particular the review by Kay should be consulted.

Carbon dioxide tension in solution in blood is a very valuable index of acid-base metabolism; it is normally measured in terms of pH under defined conditions of equilibration. The reference cited gives the details of a micro-analytical technique for its determination.

28.4. GASEOUS OXYGEN

This is best estimated by use of its paramagnetic property, which is unique in gases. The most satisfactory and simple method of utilising this is that due to Pauling, which is embodied in a number of commercial oxygen analysers. A small glass dumbbell is suspended on a taut quartz fibre in a non-uniform magnetic field. In the absence of oxygen, the dumbbell takes up a position due to the torque of the fibre alone. If oxygen is present, it is concentrated in the magnetic field, and the dumbbell is forced to rotate. The degree of its rotation depends on the amount of oxygen present; this can either be meas-ured by a mirror and light beam on a scale, or by a null method in which the torque due to the oxygen is exactly balanced by passing a current through a coil attached to the dumbbell, and the current is measured. Unfortunately, the response time of these instruments to a change in partial pressure is low, ranging from 10 sec to 1 min. For faster response, the only readily available method is the use of a suitable mass spectrometer, and this is strictly a lab-oratory technique.

28.5. GASEOUS CARBON DIOXIDE

The only specific property of carbon dioxide suitable for use in continuous flow analysis is its infrared absorption spectrum. This consists of two major groups of bands, a weakly absorbing group of three bands at 2μ, and a strongly absorbing complex group at 4μ. Two general types of infrared absorption measuring instruments are available. The first, which is rather more satisfactory in the presence of other absorbing gases, uses a narrow band optical filter to separate out one of the two groups mentioned. The 4μ group is subject to interference by several anaesthetic gases, and a glass optical system cannot be used so far into the infrared. On the other hand, the 2μ group, though readily detected by infrared sensitive photocells, is much weaker, and measurement of low concentrations of CO_2 is difficult. Some form of interrupted source of infrared illumination is usual, followed by AC amplification of the photocell output. The second method uses as detector a cell filled with CO_2, and divided by a diaphragm into two compartments, as shown in Fig. 28.2.

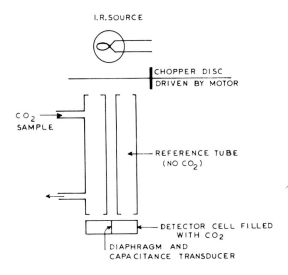

FIG. 28.2. Carbon dioxide meter.

The beam of infrared radiation, interrupted periodically by the chopper disc, is passed through both sample and reference tubes. If the sample tube contains no CO_2, equal amounts of radiation reach the two sides of the detector cell. Since the CO_2 in each side absorbs the same amount of energy, and is heated equally, there is no mean deflection of the diaphragm. If CO_2 is present in the sample tube, less energy reaches the detector cell on that side and the diaphragm is periodically deflected at the frequency set by the chopper disc. Other gases in the sample tube absorb energy too, but usually not at any wavelength which can be absorbed by the detector cell.

CO_2 analysers depending on the very poor thermal conductivity of the gas have also been used, but most of these are slow in responding to a change in partial pressure. However, instruments operating at reduced pressure can have a response time as fast as 100 msec. This method is also used for helium determinations.

28.6. NITROGEN

Nitrogen analysis is frequently required in studies on respiratory function. Most instruments for this purpose draw the gas sample into a discharge tube at a reduced pressure, excite it by an electrical discharge at high voltage, and measure the light output at a characteristic wavelength; alternatively, a mass spectrometer has been used. Gas chromatography has been widely used for respiratory research, but is slow and rather clumsy.

28.7. HYDROGEN ION CONCENTRATION

pH, which is defined as the negative logarithm of the hydrogen ion concentration in a solution, is one of the most commonly required measurements. It is normally carried out electrometrically by the use of a glass electrode, which is essentially a thin glass membrane containing a reference electrode in HCl. This membrane is of a glass permeable only to hydrogen ions, and consequently the whole composite electrode behaves as a system reversible to hydrogen. The potential of the glass electrode is measured with respect to a standard calomel electrode dipped into the solution being tested. Although very thin, the glass electrode has a very high resistance, and to obtain an accurate reading an *electrometer* circuit must be used. This usually consists of an amplifier whose first stage contains a special valve, in which every precaution has been taken to avoid leakage of electrons from or to the grid circuit. Such valves are carefully cleaned and coated with a water-repellant silicone film. They must *not be fingered* at any time. The actual potential measurement is usually carried out by a potentiometric method, using the amplifier only as a balance indicator. Each individual electrode has a small zero error potential superimposed on the pH potential; this is allowed for by a preliminary calibration in a standard buffer solution of known pH. The pH potential is also directly proportional to the absolute temperature, and a correction for this is applied to the reading.

Glass electrodes for sodium and potassium ion concentrations have also been produced; these have even higher resistances, and can be used only with special electrometers.

Further Reading

DELAHAY, *New Instrumental Methods in Electrochemistry*, Interscience, New York, 1953.

KOLTHOFF and LINGANE, *Polarography* (2nd ed.), Interscience, New York, 1952.

TSAO and VADNAY, Continuous measurement of transient blood pO_2, *J. Appl. Physiol.* **15**, 712 (1960).

COTLOVE et al., An instrument and method for chloride titration, *J. Lab. Clin. Med.* **51**, 461 (1958).

SIGGUARD, ANDERSON and ENGEL, Micro determination of pH and CO_2 tension, *Scand. J. Clin. Lab. Investigation*, 1960.

KAY, *Experimental Biology*, Chapman & Hall, London, 1964.

MELOAN and KISER, *Instrumental Analysis*, Merrill, Columbus, Ohio, 1963.

PRACTICAL

Practical work will be largely dependent on the apparatus available and the interests of each individual taking the course. Typical experiments are the estimation of sodium and potassium by flame photometer, the estimation of chloride by Cotlove's method, gas analysis of respiratory samples, and pH measurements.

INDEX